MATHEMATICAL TOPICS

Statistics: An Introduction to Tests of Significance

MATHEMATICAL TOPICS

Titles already published

An Introduction to Matrices   A. E. COULSON
An Introduction to Number Scales and Computers   F. J. BUDDEN
An Introduction to Vectors   A. E. COULSON
Statistics: An Introduction to Tests of Significance   J. K. BACKHOUSE

In Preparation

Sets and Relations   J. BUNNELL
Topology   J. E. REEVE

Statistics: An Introduction to Tests of Significance

J. K. Backhouse M.A.

TUTOR AT THE DEPARTMENT OF EDUCATION
IN THE UNIVERSITY OF OXFORD AND FORMERLY
HEAD OF THE MATHEMATICS DEPARTMENT
AT HAMPTON GRAMMAR SCHOOL

Longman

LONGMAN GROUP LIMITED
London

*Associated companies, branches and
representatives throughout the world*

First published 1967
Fifth impression 1971

ISBN 0 582 31754 1

*Printed in Hong Kong by
Sheck Wah Tong Printing Press*

Preface

The application of statistics to science, medicine, technology, sociology, industry and government is so well known that it hardly needs stressing. However, the proper use and interpretation of statistics are by no means as widespread as they should be. Many books on the subject have been published but they tend to be too elementary for the sixth-former studying mathematics, or too advanced. This volume is an attempt to introduce statistics to those whose knowledge of mathematics is approaching that required for A level of the G.C.E., whether future scientists, technologists, mathematicians, or others. In a few places, largely in Chapter 9, more advanced mathematics is assumed, but provision is made for skipping such passages. In conformity with other books in the Mathematical Topics series, a knowledge of 'modern' mathematics is not assumed.

In an introductory work such as this, the author has to be selective. What I have done is to prune the traditional topics quite severely so as to give the remainder a greater structure and unity than is sometimes apparent in works on this subject. It will be seen that the book is directed towards tests of statistical significance and that other parts of the book serve towards this end.

The individual reader has been kept in mind but, on the other hand, some exercises are more suitable for cooperative effort. A system of marking questions has been adopted to help the individual reader:

L to show that reference will be made to the question *later* in the book,

M to show that the question involves harder *mathematics* or topics not included in the text,

T to show that the question deals with *theory*, or 'bookwork' not dealt with in the text, but referred to elsewhere in the book.

Important formulae to which reference is made elsewhere in the text have been numbered and for convenience a list of them, with page references, will be found at the end of the book.

I am indebted to many people who have contributed in one way or another to the making of this book. The task of collection of data is often a laborious one and this volume would have been much poorer but for the possibility of quoting the results of workers in a variety of fields. Acknowledgement will be found where this has been done. I should also like to express my thanks to a number of individuals who in various ways have helped to bring this book into being: Mr A. R. Waltham, Mr D. F. Taylor, Mr M. J. Cohen, Mr R. Watson, Mr A. R. Tammadge, Mr M. A. Bloxham, Mrs J. E. Grant and Mrs P. M. B. Cuckney, who has read the proofs and checked the answers.

I am indebted to the Literary Executor of the Late Sir Ronald A. Fisher, F.R.S., Cambridge, to Dr Frank Yates, F.R.S., Rothamsted, and to Messrs Oliver and Boyd, Ltd., Edinburgh, for permission to reprint tables nos. III, IV and V from their book, *Statistical tables for biological, agricultural, and medical research.*

OXFORD 1967   J.K.B.

Contents

Acknowledgements

I am indebted to the following for permission to reproduce copyright material:

The Biometrika Trustees for material from *Biometrika*; Dr Arnold Brown, M.B., Ch.B., D.P.H. for material published in the *British Medical Journal*, 1 September 1962; Mr J. B. Dillane, F.R.C.S., Mr John Fry, F.R.C.S. and Dr L. Fry, M.D., M.R.C.P. for material published in the *British Medical Journal*, 29 September 1962; the Proprietors for material from *The British Journal of Educational Psychology*; the Controller of Her Majesty's Stationery Office for material from *Annual Abstract of Statistics, No. 87, Industrial Health Research Board Report 84* by E. Farmer and E. G. Chambers, *Meteorological Office: British Rainfall 1959–1960*, and The Registrar General's *Statistical Review of England and Wales 1961*; Mr D. M. Lyon and H. K. Lewis & Co. Ltd for material from *Clinical Journal 71* (1942); E. & S. Livingstone Ltd on behalf of the National Birthday Trust for material from *Perinatal Mortality* by N. R. Butler and D. G. Bonham; The Royal Society for material from the Second, Third and Fourth *Report to the Evolution Committee of the Royal Society* by W. Bateson, E. R. Saunders and R. C. Punnett; Mr T. E. Smith and the Population Investigation Committee for material from *Population Studies*, November 1960; University of London Press Ltd for material from *The Trend of Scottish Intelligence* by D. Kennedy-Fraser: *Publication No. XXX of the Scottish Council for Research in Education, 1949*, D. Van Nostrand Company, Inc. for material from *Mathematics of Statistics* by J. F. Kenney and E. S. Keeping, Copyright 1946, and Mr. S. P. T. Houldsworth and Mr. B. E. D. Cooper for material from *Pure Mathematics—A Second Course*.

Introduction

Do tall men tend to marry tall women? To what extent are the heights and weights of boys of a given age associated? Are English children more neurotic than Canadians of the same age? Do cuckoos tend to lay eggs of different sizes in nests of different species of bird? Do men who die of coronary thrombosis tend to be less fond of fatty food than average? These are just a few of the questions susceptible to statistical investigation which illustrate the ideas in this book. Statistics, in the usual sense of the word, is concerned with the collection, analysis and interpretation of numerical data—which may be drawn, for example, from medicine, physical and biological sciences, psychology, sociology and from local government and affairs of the state; indeed it is from this last that the word '*stat*istics' is derived.

'There are three kinds of lies: lies, damned lies, and statistics.' So runs the famous dictum that Mark Twain attributes to Disraeli. At the time it was made, the mathematical study of statistics had hardly begun and people had not learned about the necessary safeguards which need to be employed when they are being compiled or interpreted. At the end of last century, and at the beginning of this one, the study of statistics made tremendous strides, amongst which the development of tests of significance must be reckoned as some of the most important and useful. Such tests, some of which will be described in detail in later chapters of this book, help the subjective element in the interpretation of statistics to be reduced to a minimum, thus taking the sting out of Disraeli's dictum.

In case you have skipped the Preface, your attention is drawn to the explanation there of the letters to be found beside the numbers of certain questions in the exercises.

CHAPTER 1

Probability

1.1. If you buy a tin of peas (of stated size and brand), how much of the contents is water and how much consists of peas? If you strain and weigh the peas, you will find variations in the weight from tin to tin. Suppose, now, that the manager of the canning factory wants to know how the weight of peas in his tins varies; the only way he can be *certain* is to open and test every tin—but then he will have none unopened to sell. So he has to take a sample of tins—and this is bound to introduce an element of *chance* because of the variations from sample to sample. If it were always feasible to examine every case when we wanted to find out about something, there would be little need for the study of statistics; as it is, researchers are continually having to take samples, thus introducing chance into their experiments. This is why it is appropriate to begin this book with a chapter on probability.

Equally likely events

1.2. A formal definition of probability is notoriously difficult, so we shall start with the intuitive idea of 'equally likely events'. If, for instance, we throw a good (as opposed to biased) die, we have no reason to expect any one of the faces, say the six, rather than the others. Again, if a pack of playing cards is cut, we should say that there are equal chances of obtaining each of the four suits. These expectations depend on our experience: (1) we see no reason to expect one event rather than another, (2) in the *long run* we find that the numbers on a die, or the suits of a pack, turn up about equally often.

In case you have never tried these out, two experiments (which can be done quite quickly with cooperation between members of a class) are suggested below. It is worth while noting the use of the word *event* which is frequently used to denote some occurrence in which we are interested, e.g. a component of a machine being faulty, scoring a six with a die, spinning a head with a coin, a baby being a boy, etc.

Exercise 1a

1. L. Spin a coin a large number of times, say not less than 100. Record and graph after every ten spins the proportion of heads obtained so far.

2. L. Throw 6 or 12 dice together a large number of times. Record the number of times each of the six faces occurs. You may find it useful to tabulate and record each occurrence with a stroke:

1	2	3	4	5	6
IIII	III	++++ I	IIII	++++ II	IIII

Draw every fifth stroke in each box across the four previous strokes to assist with quick counting at the end.

Probability

1.3. Dice, coins and cards may seem rather artificial objects to discuss, but it is because of their artificiality that we feel sure about the chances involved. Historically, the mathematical theory of probability arose from a problem posed by a gambler, the Chevalier de Méré, to the mathematician Pascal about the division of stakes when a game of dice is interrupted. Apart from this historical precedent, these objects serve very well to introduce the basic ideas of probability because they are familiar to most readers.

Consider the drawing of a card at random from a pack of 52 playing cards, and suppose that we are interested in the chance of drawing an ace. There are 4 aces in the pack, so we should expect the probability of drawing an ace to be $\frac{4}{52}$. In general, if we have a number of equally likely possibilities and we are interested in the occurrence of a particular event, the *probability p* of the event is defined informally as

$$p = \frac{\text{number of possibilities in which the event occurs}}{\text{total number of possibilities}}.$$

Example 1. *Find the probability of scoring 9 with two dice.*

The first die can fall in any one of six ways and, for each of these, the second can fall in six ways. Hence there are $6 \times 6 = 36$ ways in which the two dice can fall. A score of 9 can be obtained as follows:

First die	6	5	4	3
Second die	3	4	5	6

So there are 4 ways in which a score of 9 can be obtained. Since each of the 36 possibilities is equally likely, the probability of scoring a total of 9 with two dice is $\frac{4}{36} = \frac{1}{9}$.

*Question 1. Throw two dice a large number of times and observe the proportion of times a score of 9 is obtained.

How do we know that two or more events are equally likely? An answer we might give is that we do not *know* but we see no reason why one should occur more often than the others; for example, a coin and a die are virtually symmetrical and each face may be expected to be observed approximately the same number of times in the *long run*. Or the cards of a pack of playing cards are so closely alike that we should expect each card to appear equally often when we make a large number of draws. However, if we spin a coin or throw a die many times, as in Exercise 1a, we should not expect each face to appear *exactly* the same number of times. Some writers call the observed proportion of occurrences of an event the 'experimental probability' but we shall reserve the term 'probability' for what is *expected* and use 'proportion' for what is *observed*. It may be, of course, that we make a conjecture such as, 'The probability in Great Britain that an unborn baby will be a boy is $\frac{1}{2}$', which is demonstrably false. The case in point may be decided by reference to the Registrar General's annual returns, but it may also be shown to be highly improbable even when a sample is taken (see §5.3).

Exercise 1b

1. Find the probability of drawing a court card (king, queen, knave) from a pack of 52 playing cards.

2. 'If I take a book and pick a letter at random with a pin, the chance that it is a vowel is 5/26.' Is this statement true or false? Give your reasons.

3. What are the probabilities of the last digit of a telephone number picked at random being 0, 1, 2, ..., 9? Would the same hold for the first digit?

4. Find the probabilities of scoring 2, 3, 4, 5, 6, 7, 8, (9), 10, 11, 12 with two dice. What is their sum?

5. There are four routes between A and B, none of which intersect except at A and B. If one man starts from A and another from B by routes chosen at random, what is the probability that they meet?

Complementary probability

1.4. We found in Example 1 that there are 4 ways of scoring 9 with two dice. Since two dice may fall in 36 ways, there are 32 ways in which 9 is

---

* These questions should be worked when they are encountered in reading the text.

not scored. The probability of obtaining a score of 9 is $p=\frac{4}{36}=\frac{1}{9}$; the *complementary probability*, i. e., the probability of *not* obtaining a score of 9, $q=\frac{32}{36}=\frac{8}{9}$. Note particularly that $p+q=1$. In general if p is the probability that an event occurs out of a number of equally likely possibilities

$$p = \frac{\text{number of possibilities in which the event occurs}}{\text{total number of possibilities}}$$

$$q = \frac{\text{number of possibilities in which the event does not occur}}{\text{total number of possibilities}}$$

but the event either does or does not occur so that the sum of the numerators on the right-hand side is the total number of possibilities. Therefore

$$p+q = 1 \qquad (1)$$

Note that:

if $p=0$, the event *never* occurs (an impossibility),
if $p=1$, the event *always* occurs (a certainty),

and that always $0 \leqslant p \leqslant 1$.

Exercise 1c

1. Find the probability of (i) drawing a spade from a pack of playing cards, (ii) not drawing a spade from the same pack.

2. Find the probability of scoring (i) less than 18, (ii) less than 17, when three dice are thrown together.

3. In how many different ways can a halfpenny, a penny and a shilling fall when they are spun? What is the probability of obtaining less than 3 heads?

Mutually exclusive events

1.5. A coin cannot fall 'heads' and 'tails' simultaneously: the two events are said to be *mutually exclusive*. Again, the events of scoring 4 with a die and scoring a multiple of 3 with the same die cannot take place together and so are mutually exclusive. On the other hand, the events that a card drawn from a pack of playing cards should be an ace and that it should be a spade are not mutually exclusive because we might draw the ace of spades.

Exercise 1d

1. Which of the following pairs of events are mutually exclusive?

(i) A town is (a) in France, (b) in Europe.
(ii) A number is (a) even, (b) prime.
(iii) A vehicle (a) is a trailer, (b) has two wheels.

(iv) A tree is (a) evergreen, (b) deciduous.

(v) A number is (a) a square, (b) a cube.

(vi) Two lines are (a) perpendicular, (b) parallel.

Addition of probabilities

1.6. Some letters (a, e, i, o, u) are vowels; some others (p, b, f, v, m, w) are labials. If we choose a letter at random from the alphabet, the probability of choosing a vowel is $\frac{5}{26}$ and the probability of choosing a labial is $\frac{6}{26}$. Further, the probability of choosing either a vowel or a labial is $\frac{11}{26}$.

In general, if there are n possibilities, of which n_A give an event A and n_B give an event B, the probability of either the event A or the event B

$$p = \frac{n_A + n_B}{n}$$

provided the events A and B are mutually exclusive.

$$\therefore p = \frac{n_A}{n} + \frac{n_B}{n}$$

$$\therefore p = p_A + p_B \qquad (2)$$

where p_A, p_B are the probabilities of the events A and B.

Exercise 1e

1. Write down the result **(2)** in your own words, without using mathematical symbols, but incorporating the restriction on the events A and B.

2. A number is drawn at random from 1, 2, ..., 9, 10. What is the probability that the number drawn is (i) a multiple of 3, (ii) a multiple of 7, (iii) a multiple of either 3 or 7?

3. With the same data as in No. 2, what is the probability that the number drawn is (i) a multiple of 2, (ii) a multiple of 5? Why can we not add these probabilities to find the probability that the number is a multiple of either 2 or 5?

4. Four unlike coins are spun. In how many ways can they come down? What is the probability of obtaining (i) 4 heads, (ii) either 4 heads or 4 tails?

5. Three dice are thrown together. What is the probability of obtaining (i) three sixes, (ii) exactly two sixes, (iii) more than one six?

6. T. Generalise formula **(2)** to m mutually exclusive events.

Those readers who are familiar with set notation may find it illuminating in the interpretation of Exercise 1e, No. 3; other readers should skip to §1.7. Consider the universal set

$$\mathscr{E} = \{1, 2, 3, 4, 5, 6, 7, 8, 9, 10\}$$

and let

$$A = \{\text{multiples of 2}\}$$

$$B = \{\text{multiples of 5}\}$$

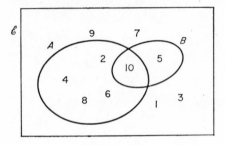

Fig. 1.1

If we denote by $p(X)$ the probability that a number from set X should be drawn,

$$p(A \cup B) = \tfrac{6}{10}, \quad p(A) = \tfrac{5}{10}, \quad p(B) = \tfrac{2}{10}, \quad p(A \cap B) = \tfrac{1}{10}$$

so that, in this case,

$$p(A \cup B) = p(A) + p(B) - p(A \cap B) \tag{i}$$

Question 2. Verify the relationship (i) above by considering a general case in which there are a elements in set A, b in set B, c in $A \cap B$ and n in the universal set.

In the case of formula (2) it will be seen that the sets

$$A = \{a, e, i, o, u\}$$

$$B = \{p, b, f, v, m, w\}$$

are disjoint, in which case **(2)** may be written

$$p(A \cup B) = p(A) + p(B)$$

which is a special case of (i).

Independent events

1.7. If I spin a coin and it comes down 'heads', experience tells me that a head and a tail are equally likely on the next spin. (If you do not believe this, try it out a large number of times.) Again, if I throw a die and obtain a six, this will make no difference to the probability of drawing an ace from a pack of cards. Such pairs of events are called *independent*. On the other hand, if I draw a card from a pack of playing cards and do not replace it, this will alter the probability that the second card drawn is an ace; these events therefore are not independent.

Exercise 1f

1. When drawing two cards from a pack of playing cards, what precautions should be taken to ensure that the two events are independent?

2. A die is weighted to give a six more frequently than one time in six in a long run of throws. If I make two throws with this die, will the events be independent?

3. If a marksman fires two shots at a target with a rifle he has never used before, will the positions of the bullet holes on the target be independent?

Multiplication of probabilities

1.8. Consider two events:

(1) drawing an ace from a pack of playing cards,

(2) throwing a six with a die.

In the first case, there are 4 aces in the 52 cards of the pack, so that the probability of drawing an ace $p_1 = \frac{4}{52}$. The probability of throwing a six $p_2 = \frac{1}{6}$.

Now suppose that a card is drawn and a die is thrown. What is the probability p that both an ace is drawn and a six is thrown? For each of the 52 cards that may be drawn, the die may fall in 6 different ways, giving 52×6 possibilities. Of these, 4 give both an ace and a six, so that the probability of this event $p = 4/(52 \times 6)$. Note that (i) the two events are independent (i.e. the occurrence of one does not affect the probability of the other), and (ii) $p = p_1 \times p_2$.

In general, consider two independent events (1) and (2) which may arise in respectively n_1, n_2 ways out of N_1, N_2 equally likely possibilities. The number of combinations of possibilities is $N_1 N_2$ and of these the events

(1) and (2) occur together $n_1 n_2$ times. Therefore the probability of both events taking place

$$p = \frac{n_1 n_2}{N_1 N_2}$$

$$\therefore p = p_1 p_2 \tag{3}$$

where p_1, p_2 are the probabilities of the independent events (1) and (2).

Question 3. Generalise formula (3) to m independent events.

Example 2. *A die is thrown three times. What are the probabilities of obtaining a six (i) each time, (ii) only on the third throw?*

(i) The probability of throwing a six is $\frac{1}{6}$; the three throws are independent and so the probability of throwing three sixes is

$$\tfrac{1}{6} \times \tfrac{1}{6} \times \tfrac{1}{6} = \tfrac{1}{216}$$

(ii) The probability of throwing a six is $\frac{1}{6}$ so by (1) the probability of not throwing a six is $\frac{5}{6}$. The first two throws are independent, therefore the probability that they do not produce sixes is $\frac{5}{6} \times \frac{5}{6}$. The third throw is independent of the first two, so the probability that there is a six only on the third throw is

$$\tfrac{5}{6} \times \tfrac{5}{6} \times \tfrac{1}{6} = \tfrac{25}{216}$$

Exercise 1g

1. A card is drawn from a pack of playing cards and replaced; then another draw is made. What is the probability of drawing (i) two aces (ii) two spades?

2. Two letters are drawn from the alphabet so that every letter has an equal chance of selection on both occasions. What is the probability of drawing (i) two vowels (a, e, i, o, u), (ii) two labials (p, b, f, v, m, w), (iii) a vowel and then a labial?

3. If I draw lots with three other people for three tickets, what is the chance that I get (i) all of them, (ii) only the last, (iii) just one ticket?

4. In a large batch of seed,† 75 per cent of the plants which could be grown from it would have red flowers and the rest white. Find the probability that two plants grown from it should have flowers of the same colour.

5. If 5 per cent of a consignment of eggs are bad, estimate the chance that half a dozen chosen at random contains at least one bad egg. (*Hint*: Start by finding the probability that none are bad.)

† The batch is described as 'large' so that you may assume the probability to be the same for both plants.

Conditional probabilities

1.9. The result **(3)** (p. 8) may be extended to the case where p_1 is the probability of the first event and p_2 is the probability of the second *when the first has taken place*. A similar argument shows that the probability that both events should take place is p_1p_2.

Example 3. *A card is drawn from a pack of playing cards and then another card is drawn without the first being replaced. What is the probability of drawing (i) two aces, (ii) two spades.* (Compare Exercise 1g, No. 1.)

(i) The probability that the first card is an ace is $\frac{4}{52}$. When an ace has been drawn there are three aces in the 51 cards left, therefore the probability that the second card should also be an ace is $\frac{3}{51}$. Hence the probability that both cards are aces is

$$\tfrac{4}{52} \times \tfrac{3}{51} = \tfrac{1}{13} \times \tfrac{1}{17} = \tfrac{1}{221}.$$

(ii) The probability that the first card is a spade is $\frac{13}{52}$. The probability that the second card should also be a spade is $\frac{12}{51}$. Therefore the probability that both cards should be spades is

$$\tfrac{13}{52} \times \tfrac{12}{51} = \tfrac{1}{17}.$$

Exercise 1h

1. Nine equal balls, four black and the rest white, are placed in a bag. If two are drawn at random, what is the probability that both should be (i) black, (ii) white?

2. In a packet of sweets there are 5 red, 5 brown, 5 yellow, 5 white, 5 orange What is the probability that a child taking two without looking should take (i) 2 red, (ii) 2 the same colour?

3. Four digits are chosen at random: what is the probability that they are all different? Check your result with 100 groups of 4 final digits chosen from a telephone directory.

Introducing the binomial distribution

1.10. This distribution plays an important part in this book; a fuller treatment of it will be given later but the following example provides a suitable conclusion to this chapter since it revises all the work so far.

Example 4. *Find the probabilities of obtaining* 0, 1, 2, 3 *sixes when three dice are thrown.*

The probability of throwing a six with a given die is $\frac{1}{6}$; that of not throwing a six with it is $\frac{5}{6}$.

9

Case (*i*): no six obtained. The probability of each die not being a six is $\frac{5}{6}$; the events are independent, therefore the probability of no six is $\frac{5}{6} \times \frac{5}{6} \times \frac{5}{6} = (\frac{5}{6})^3$.

Case (*ii*): one six obtained. Suppose the first die gives a six and the other two do not; the events are independent, so the probability that only the first is a six is $\frac{1}{6} \times \frac{5}{6} \times \frac{5}{6} = \frac{1}{6}(\frac{5}{6})^2$.

If only the second die is a six, we again get $\frac{1}{6}(\frac{5}{6})^2$, and if only the third die is a six, we also get $\frac{1}{6}(\frac{5}{6})^2$.

Now these three ways of obtaining one six in three throws are mutually exclusive; we may therefore add the probabilities to obtain $3 \times \frac{1}{6}(\frac{5}{6})^2$ as the probability of obtaining just one six.

Case (*iii*): two sixes obtained. Suppose the first die is not a six and the other two are sixes, then the corresponding probability is $\frac{5}{6} \times \frac{1}{6} \times \frac{1}{6}$. By an argument similar to that in Case (ii), we find that the probability of obtaining just two sixes is $3 \times \frac{5}{6}(\frac{1}{6})^2$.

Case (*iv*): three sixes obtained. The probability of each die being a six is $\frac{1}{6}$; the events are independent, therefore the probability of three sixes is $(\frac{1}{6})^3$.

If these probabilities are written in succession:

$$(\tfrac{5}{6})^3, \quad 3(\tfrac{5}{6})^2(\tfrac{1}{6}), \quad 3(\tfrac{5}{6})(\tfrac{1}{6})^2, \quad (\tfrac{1}{6})^3,$$

the reader may notice that they are the four terms of the expansion of $(q+p)^3$ where $q = \frac{5}{6}$, $p = \frac{1}{6}$. This suggestive observation is followed up in the first few questions in Exercise 1i; the later ones are concerned with the work of the chapter but are not so directly relevant to the development later in the book.

Exercise 1i

1. Show that the sum of the probabilities in Example 4 is 1.

2. When propagating a certain bush by cuttings, the probability that a cutting strikes is $\frac{2}{3}$. Find the probabilities of 0, 1, 2 cuttings striking when 2 cuttings are taken.

3. If 4 different coins are spun, in how many ways can two come down heads and the other two tails? Find the probabilities of obtaining 0, 1, 2, 3, 4 heads when 4 coins are spun together.

4. Check that the sums of the probabilities in Nos. 2 and 3 are both 1. Can both sets of probabilities be expressed as the terms of binomial expansions?

5. Obtain the probabilities of 0, 1, 2, 3 wins in a game of chance played three times when the probability of a win on each occasion is p.

6. Playing bridge, I have won the bidding and have five trumps while dummy has four. Compare the probabilities of my opponents having (i) two trumps each and (ii) one having three while the other has one.

7. When three men shoot at a target, the probabilities that each hits it are $\frac{2}{3}, \frac{3}{4}, \frac{2}{5}$. What is the probability that at least one of them hits the target? (*Hint*: Use equation (1).)

8. M. Five per cent of the tickets in a lottery have prizes. How many tickets should I buy in order that the probability of receiving a prize should be greater than 90 per cent?

9. M. In a certain strain of Aster, the chance that a seed produces pink flowers is $\frac{1}{4}$. How many seeds should I sow in order that the probability of obtaining at least one pink flower should be greater than 99 per cent?

10. M. A and B each place a stake on the table; the first to throw a six with a single die takes all the money. If A throws first, what are their respective chances of winning?

11. M. A and B fight a duel with pistols, firing simultaneously. The chance that A kills B with any one shot is $\frac{1}{4}$ and the chance that B kills A is $\frac{2}{5}$. What is the chance that both are alive after the second round? What are their respective chances of survival in a duel to the death?

12. M. Three musketeers playing with two dice have a stake of three louis d'or on the table to be taken by the first to throw a double six. They are throwing in the order A, B, C when they are interrupted by a call to duty from which they may not all return. If B was just about to throw, how should they divide the stake?

CHAPTER 2

Arithmetic mean

2.1. The word 'average' will be familiar to you: what you may not know is that there are several averages, each used on certain occasions. For the purposes of this book we shall only be using the usual 'average', or 'arithmetic mean', and the main part of this chapter is concerned with the calculation of this when large numbers of observations are made. However, some reference should be made to two other averages, the median and mode.

The median of a triangle divides its area into two equal parts; in the same way the *median* of the following set of ages, arranged in order of magnitude,

$$12, 14, 17, 23, 42, 45, 61,$$

is the age 23 which has as many ages in the set below it as above it. (If there had been an even number of ages, we should have taken half the sum of the two central ones.)

The *mode* is, in loose terms, the 'most popular' (cf. 'in the mode') value of the variable being measured. Thus in Table 2, p. 16, the number of cells observed most frequently is 4, and so 4 cells is the mode.

The reasons for using the mean, rather than median or mode, in this book cannot be gone into at this stage but it is hoped that they will emerge in Chapters 3 and 5.

The arithmetic mean

2.2. The average weight of the Oxford boat race crew excluding the cox in 1965 was

$$\frac{176+190+180+190+184+201+182+187}{8} = 186\tfrac{1}{4} \text{ lb}$$

From the way in which the calculation is written out, it is clear that the weights of the eight oarsmen have been added together and the sum divided by eight. In general, if we have n values of a variable, $x_1, x_2, \ldots, x_n$ their *arithmetic mean* (or more briefly, their *mean*)

$$\bar{x} = \frac{x_1+x_2+\ldots+x_n}{n}$$

or, using the Σ notation,

$$\bar{x} = \frac{\sum\limits_{1}^{n} x_i}{n}$$

In practice we shall not cause confusion by writing this more simply as

$$\bar{x} = \frac{\sum x}{n} \tag{4}$$

The symbol m is also used to denote the mean; for the moment we shall use $\bar{x}$.

Exercise 2a

1. (For discussion.) What does an average measure, or represent?

2. The 1965 Oxford cox weighed 126 lb (see further data above); what was the average weight of the nine men in the boat?

The nine men in the 1965 Cambridge boat had an average weight of $183\frac{1}{3}$ lb. The eight oarsmen had an average weight of $190\frac{1}{4}$ lb; how much did the cox weigh?

3. Write with the Σ notation:

(i) $x_1^2 + x_2^2 + \ldots + x_n^2$;

(ii) $\dfrac{x_1 - a}{n} + \dfrac{x_2 - a}{n} + \ldots + \dfrac{x_n - a}{n}$.

4. Write in expanded form, as in No. 3:

(i) $\sum (x-a)^2$;

(ii) $\sum \dfrac{x^2 - a^2}{n}$.

5. Show that

$$\sum (x - \bar{x}) = 0 = \frac{\sum (x - \bar{x})}{n} = \sum \frac{x - \bar{x}}{n} \quad \text{where } \bar{x} = \frac{\sum x}{n}.$$

Use of an arbitrary origin

2.3. The calculation of a mean is often considerably eased by taking the deviations (differences with negative signs retained) from some arbitrary value, or *arbitrary origin*.

For instance, here are the ages in years and months of a sixth-form class:

16.3, 15.6, 15.11, 16.11, 16.5, 16.8, 16.9, 17.1, 15.4, 17.0, 16.9, 17.1, 17.1

We *could* find the total age of the class in years and months, and hence find the average age, but it is simpler to proceed as follows: first choose some age from which to find the deviations (make a guess at the average or a bit below it), say 16 yr 5 mo; next find the deviation of each age from this value in months:

$$-2, \quad -11, \quad -6, \quad 6, \quad 0, \quad 3, \quad 4, \quad 8, \quad -13, \quad 7, \quad 4, \quad 8, \quad 8$$

then find the average deviation:

$$\frac{-2-11-6+6+0+3+4+8-13+7+4+8+8}{13} = \frac{16}{13} = 1{\cdot}23 \text{ mo.}$$

Finally, add this average deviation to the arbitrary origin of 16 yr 5 mo to find the average age, 16 yr 6 mo, to the nearest month.

In general, if we have n values of a variable $x_1, x_2, \ldots, x_n$ and take their deviations from an arbitrary origin x, the mean of the deviations is

$$\frac{1}{n}\{(x_1-x_0)+(x_2-x_0)+\ldots+(x_n-x_0)\} = \frac{1}{n}\sum (x-x_0)$$

Then the mean $\bar{x}$ is given by

$$\bar{x} = x_0 + \frac{1}{n}\sum (x-x_0) \qquad\qquad (5)$$

This may be intuitively obvious to some readers, but here is a proof:

$$\frac{1}{n}\sum (x-x_0) = \frac{1}{n}\{(x_1-x_0)+(x_2-x_0)+\ldots+(x_n-x_0)\}$$

$$= \frac{1}{n}(x_1+x_2+\ldots+x_n-nx_0)$$

$$= \frac{1}{n}\sum (x)-x_0$$

$$= \bar{x}-x_0 \qquad\qquad \text{(using (4))}$$

$$\therefore \bar{x} = x_0 + \frac{1}{n}\sum (x-x_0)$$

It is worth remarking at this stage that if a proof using the $\sum$ notation seems difficult, the difficulty may resolve itself if the formulae concerned are written out in full.

Exercise 2b

1. Express formula (5) in your own words without using mathematical symbols.

2. Find the mean age, height, or weight of the members of your class or form. If you are working on your own and cannot get hold of this data easily, find the mean of the following heights, given to the nearest inch:

6 ft 1 in., 5 ft 7 in., 5 ft 10 in., 5 ft 8 in., 6 ft 0 in.,
5 ft 8 in., 5 ft 9 in., 5 ft 10 in., 5 ft 11 in., 5 ft 9 in.

(Find the deviations from an arbitrary origin.)

3. Estimate the length of your classroom to the nearest foot. Find the mean of the class's estimates. Compare this with the measured length. The individual reader can find the mean of the following estimates of the length of a lecture room given in feet:

26, 32, 50, 36, 40, 45, 28, 30, 32, 36, 39, 27, 33, 36, 40.

Frequency distributions

2.4. The raw material for a statistical analysis consists of a number of observations, each of which may take a considerable time to make. For instance, if the marks of an examination are to be analysed, each script may have taken one examiner 10 minutes to mark, so that 100 000 scripts (marked by a number of examiners) may together take somewhere in the region of 2 years work. In comparison with this, the statistical analysis takes very little time. This is worth bearing in mind as you read through this book—indeed you might remember that usually the first stage of the analysis has been done for you already.

Here, for example, is a set of observations from a celebrated paper by W. S. Gosset, who wrote under the name of 'Student'. Note the close observation under the microscope that was needed for each entry.

In Table 1 is shown the result of counting the number of yeast cells in each of 400 squares into which a sq. mm was divided—the counting being done, of course, with the assistance of a microscope. As it stands, it is difficult to get much impression of the way in which the numbers of cells per square varies, so we count the number of times 1, 2, ..., 11, 12 occurs in Table 1 and tabulate the result in Table 2. Here we need to introduce two terms or we shall get muddled as to whether we are talking about the number of cells or the number of times each number of cells appears. The variable we count or measure is called the *variate* and is usually denoted by x: in this case the variate is the number of yeast cells on one of the 400 squares, and may be seen to take values from 1 to 12. The number of times any value (or range of values in later work) of the variate occurs is called its *frequency* and is denoted by f; in Table 2 we see that the frequency varies from 2 to 86. The total frequency of the distribution will be denoted by *n* so that here *n* = 400 and in general

$$\Sigma f = n \qquad (6)$$

Distribution of yeast cells over 1 sq. mm divided into 400 squares. ('Student', *Biometrika*, 5, 359.)

2	2	4	4	4	5	2	4	7	7	4	7	5	2	8	6	7	4	3 ·	4
3	3	2	4	2	5	4	2	8	6	3	6	6	10	8	3	5	6	4	4
7	9	5	2	7	4	4	2	4	4	4	3	5	6	5	4	1	4	2	6
4	1	4	7	3	2	3	5	8	2	9	5	3	9	5	5	2	4	3	4
4	1	5	9	3	4	4	6	6	5	4	6	5	5	4	3	5	9	6	4
4	4	5	10	4	4	3	8	3	2	1	4	1	5	6	4	2	3	3	3
3	7	4	5	1	8	5	7	9	5	8	9	5	6	6	4	3	7	4	4
7	5	6	3	6	7	4	5	8	6	3	3	4	3	7	4	4	4	5	3
8	10	6	3	3	6	5	2	5	3	11	3	7	4	7	3	5	5	3	4
1	3	7	2	5	5	5	3	3	4	6	5	6	1	6	4	4	4	6	4
4	2	5	4	8 ·	6	3	4	6	5	2	6	6	1	2	2	2	5	2	2
5	9	3	5	6	4	6	5	7	1	3	6	5	4	2	8	9	5	4	3
2	2	11	4	6	6	4	6	2	5	3	5	7	2	6	5	5	1	2	7
5	12	5	8	2	4	2	1	6	4	5	1	2	9	1	3	4	7	3	6
5	6	5	4	4	5	2	7	6	2	7	3	5	4	4	5	4	7	5	4
8	4	6	6	5	3	3	5	7	4	5	5	5	6	10	2	3	8	3	5
6	6	4	2	6	6	7	5	4	5	8	6	7	6	4	2	6	1	1	4
7	2	5	7	4	6	4	5	1	5	10	8	7	5	4	6	4	4	7	5
4	3	1	6	2	5	3	3	3	7	4	3	7	8	4	7	3	1	4	4
7	6	7	2	4	5	1	3	12	4	2	2	8	7	6	7	6	3	5	4

Table 1

Table 2 shows the *frequency distribution* of the number of yeast cells over 1 sq. mm divided into 400 squares.

No. of cells	1	2	3	4	5	6	7	8	9	10	11	12
Frequency	20	43	53	86	70	54	37	18	10	5	2	2

Table 2

Question 1. Check Table 2 by the method indicated in Exercise 1a, No. 2.

The frequency distribution in Table 2 gives a much better impression of the distribution than Table 1 but a graph helps us to assimilate the information still more quickly. Fig. 2.1 shows a graph of the distribution; this shows clearly that the distribution is lacking in symmetry, or *skew*. This type of graph is called a *histogram*; the variate is represented on the

x-axis and the frequency is represented by the area of a rectangle with its base on the corresponding part of the x-axis.

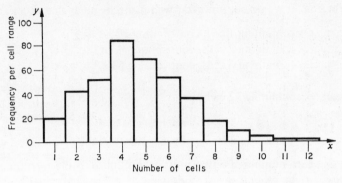

Fig. 2.1

In this particular example, the intervals on the x-axis are equal and so the heights of the rectangles are proportional to the frequencies. Suppose, however, that the frequency distribution had been given as follows:

No. of cells	1 or 2	3	4	5	6	7	8 to 12
Frequency	63	53	86	70	54	37	37

Then the heights of the first and last rectangles would have had to have been drawn so that the *areas* of these rectangles represented the frequencies 63 and 37; this is shown in Fig. 2.2. This representation by area is a point to which we shall return in Chapter 4.

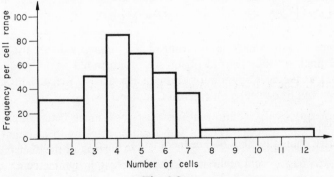

Fig. 2.2

17

Now what is the mean of the distribution? We could find this out from the original array using $\bar{x} = \dfrac{1}{n} \sum x$ **(4)** but it is easier to use the frequency distribution. If we do so, however, we must remember that there are:

20 squares containing 1 cell, contributing 20×1 to $\sum x$
43 squares containing 2 cells, contributing 43×2 to $\sum x$
53 squares containing 3 cells, contributing 53×3 to $\sum x$

. . . .

2 squares containing 12 cells, contributing 2×12 to $\sum x$.

$$\bar{x} = \tfrac{1}{400}(20 \times 1 + 43 \times 2 + 53 \times 3 + 86 \times 4 + 70 \times 5 + 54 \times 6$$
$$+ 37 \times 7 + 18 \times 8 + 10 \times 9 + 5 \times 10 + 2 \times 11 + 2 \times 12).$$

Note that each number of cells x must be multiplied by the corresponding frequency f. In general terms, the mean of a frequency distribution is given by the formula

$$\bar{x} = \frac{1}{n} \sum fx, \qquad (4a)$$

where $n = \sum f$. This, it must be emphasised, is simply restating **(4)** $\bar{x} = \dfrac{1}{n} \sum x$ in a slightly different way which is more appropriate when we are dealing with frequency distributions.

An analogy with mechanics is worth noting:

Statistics	*Mechanics*
frequency f	mass m
total frequency n	total mass M
mean $\bar{x}$	x-coordinate of centroid $\bar{x}$
$\bar{x} = \dfrac{1}{n} \sum fx$	$\bar{x} = \dfrac{1}{M} \sum mx$
$n = \sum f$	$M = \sum m$

This means that we can regard the mean of a frequency distribution as the x-coordinate of the centroid of masses proportional to the frequencies situated at the corresponding points on the axis of the variate x. This analogy will be developed further in Chapter 3.

Exercise 2c

1. Verify (mentally) that **(4a)** reduces to **(4)** when every value of f is 1.

2. In 75 phagocytic counts at a London hospital, the frequency distribution of the number of bacilli per cell was as follows. Find the mean number of bacilli per cell. (M. Greenwood, and J. D. C. White, *Biometrika* 6, 382.)

No. of bacilli per cell	0	1	2	3	4	5	6	7	8	9	10	11	12
Frequency	2	3	9	11	11	14	9	9	3	3	1	0	0

3. 166 London omnibus drivers, who were exposed to risk for a year, had the following distribution of accidents. Calculate the mean number of accidents per driver. (E. Farmer, and E. G. Chambers, *A study of accident proneness among motor drivers.*)

No. of accidents	0	1	2	3	4	5	6	7	8
No. of drivers	45	36	40	19	12	8	3	2	1

4. Display the data of Exercise 2e, No. 12 as histograms.

Use of an arbitrary origin

2.5. The arithmetic necessary for calculating the mean of the distribution given in Table 2, p. 16, can be simplified by using an arbitrary origin. If you have a calculating machine available, you may not need to use this method but you are advised not to skip this section because the idea of an arbitrary origin leads to an important piece of work in the next chapter.

It is natural to adapt the formula

$$\bar{x} = x_0 + \frac{1}{n} \sum (x - x_0) \tag{5}$$

to our present purposes. We want, as in §2.3, to find the mean of the deviations from x_0, the arbitrary origin. But this time we must remember to multiply each deviation by the corresponding frequency, just as we did on p. 18. If we do this, we shall calculate the mean of a frequency distribution by

$$\bar{x} = x_0 + \frac{1}{n} \sum f(x - x_0) \tag{5a}$$

where $n = \sum f$. This is simply restating formula (5) in a slightly different way appropriate to frequency distributions.

Example 1. *Calculate the mean number of cells per square from the frequency distribution given in Table 2, p. 16.*

(Addition tends to be done more accurately if the data is written in columns. Check your addition by adding both up and down columns.)

A look at the distribution suggests that the mean is between 4 and 5 cells per square, so we take 4 as the arbitrary origin x_0. As always, we use x for the variate (number of cells per square) and f for the frequency.

x	f	$x-x_0$	$f(x-x_0)$*	
0	0	-4	0	
1	20	-3	-60	
2	43	-2	-86	
3	53	-1	-53	
				-199
$x_0 =$ 4	86	0	0	
5	70	1	70	
6	54	2	108	
7	37	3	111	
8	18	4	72	
9	10	5	50	
10	5	6	30	
11	2	7	14	
12	2	8	16	
				$+471$
	$\Sigma f = 400$		$\Sigma f(x-x_0) = 272$	

(1) Under the heading '$x-x_0$' we write the result of subtracting 4 from each value of x (since $x_0=4$).

(2) Under $f(x-x_0)$ we write the result of multiplying each value of f by the corresponding value of $(x-x_0)$.

(3) The total deviation from 4 is the sum of the numbers in the column under $f(x-x_0)$. You may find it convenient to write down the sums of the negative and positive deviations separately, as has been done on the right. The total deviation is 272.

(4) The mean of the deviations from 4 is $\frac{272}{400}=0\cdot68$.

(5) The mean is $4+0\cdot68=4\cdot68$ cells per square.

In the next example we prove a result which is sufficiently important later on to be included as one of the numbered formulae.

* There should be no confusion with the function notation since ϕ will be used instead of f for a function.

Example 2. *Prove that*

$$\Sigma f(x - \bar{x}) = 0 \tag{4b}$$

$$\Sigma f(x - \bar{x}) = \Sigma (fx - f\bar{x})$$

$$= \Sigma fx - \Sigma f\bar{x}$$

Now by **(4a)** $\qquad \Sigma fx = n\bar{x}$

and, since $\bar{x}$ is a constant factor in the summation, we may also rewrite $\Sigma f\bar{x} = \bar{x} \Sigma f$. But $\Sigma f = n$,

$$\therefore \Sigma f\bar{x} = \bar{x}n$$

$$\therefore \Sigma f(x - \bar{x}) = n\bar{x} - \bar{x}n = 0$$

Exercise 2d

1. Prove the result of Example 2 by a suitable substitution in **(5a)**.

2. Prove the result **(5a)**.

3. L. *The frequency distribution of the number of peas per pod in 153 pods of sugar peas is given below. Calculate the mean number of peas per pod.

No. of peas per pod	1	2	3	4	5	6	7	8
Frequency	1	10	24	33	34	30	19	2

4. L. *When four dice are thrown simultaneously 81 times, the theoretical frequency distribution of the number of dice showing a 5 or a 6 is:

No. scoring 5 or 6	0	1	2	3	4
Frequency	16	32	24	8	1

What would you expect to be the mean number of dice showing 5 or 6 when four dice are thrown together? Verify your guess by calculating the mean of the distribution.

Grouped frequency distributions

2.6. The distributions in §§ 2.4 and 2.5 are all concerned with what is called a *discrete* variate. This is a variate which can only take a restricted number of isolated values—in fact throughout those sections the variate only takes positive integral values over a limited range. On the

* You are advised to leave space for a column of working on the right and for further working below.

other hand, a variable such as height, weight or age can take any value over a certain range found in nature. Such a variate is termed *continuous* and we now turn to the question of estimating the mean of a frequency distribution of a continuous variate.

Suppose that the heights of a large number of people are measured, the height of any one person depends on the way they hold themselves and it is unrealistic to measure them to the nearest hundredth of an inch; often it is done to the nearest quarter inch below the person's height. Thus anyone with height in the interval $71\frac{1}{2} \leqslant x < 71\frac{3}{4}$ in. would be recorded as having a height of $71\frac{1}{2}$ in. So when many people are measured we inevitably group together the heights of people with nearly the same height. Now if we are looking at a frequency distribution it is usually convenient to have the heights grouped together into between 10 and 20 groups; if there are too few groups, the grouping will reduce the amount of information that could have been given; if there are too many groups, it is difficult to assimilate the information from them, and chance irregularities in the distribution may show up to a greater extent.

Now consider the following distribution of the weights of babies (other than twins and triplets) born in England, Scotland and Wales during the week 3–9 March 1958. (N. R. Butler, and D. G. Bonham, *Perinatal mortality*, 133.)

Weight (g)	1000 & under	1001– 1500	1501– 2000	2001– 2500	2501– 3000	3001– 3500	3501– 4000	Over 4000	Total
Frequency	50	100	173	731	3060	6104	4584	1586	16994

In order to calculate the mean weight of these babies we shall have to make some assumption about the way the weights are distributed over each of these intervals. The simplest assumption to make is that the weights are uniformly distributed over each interval so that in effect we take all the weights in any interval to be equal to the value of the variate at the mid-point of the interval. Admittedly, this will introduce a certain inaccuracy into the calculation but in each interval the over-estimates of the values below the mid-value will tend to be cancelled out by the under-estimates of the values above the mid-values. (Under certain conditions corrections, known as 'Sheppard's corrections', can be made to allow for the inaccuracy introduced; this however, will not be discussed in this book.) Now if we consider the interval '1001–1500', what exactly is the mid-value? If the weights were measured to the nearest gramme, the interval may be written as

$$1000 \cdot 5 \leqslant x < 1500 \cdot 5 \quad (\text{mid-value } 1250 \cdot 5)$$

but, if the weights are given in complete grammes, the interval would be

$$1001 \leqslant x < 1501 \quad \text{(mid-value 1251)}$$

In fact, the babies were weighed in lb and oz by many different midwives and it is not stated what convention was followed when these weights were converted into grammes. Of course, the difference of $\frac{1}{2}$ g is not important in the present case but it is worth bearing in mind that your own observations should be recorded unambiguously. Let us take the mid-values of the intervals to be 1250·5 etc., then we may calculate the mean in the same way as we did in Example 1. With no further information available, we arbitrarily take the first and last mid-values to be 750·5 g and 4250·5 g. When we divide by $n=16388$, the error introduced by the first will be insignificant; that introduced by the latter will be larger and it will probably make the estimate of the mean a little too large because there are likely to be fewer weights above the mid-value than below for the heaviest group.

mid-value x	frequency f	$x - x_0$	$f(x - x_0)$
750·5	50	−2500	−125 000
1250·5	100	−2000	−200 000
1750·5	173	−1500	−259 500
2250·5	731	−1000	−731 000
2750·5	3060	−500	−1 530 000
$x_0 = $ 3250·5	6104	0	0
3750·5	4584	500	2 292 000
4250·5	1586	1000	1 586 000
	$n = 16388$		$\sum f(x - x_0) = 1 032 500$

$$\bar{x} = x_0 + \frac{1}{n}\sum f(x - x_0) \tag{5a}$$

$$= 3250{\cdot}5 + \frac{1 032 500}{16 388}$$

$$= 3250{\cdot}5 + 63{\cdot}00$$

$$\therefore \bar{x} = 3314 \text{ g}$$

The numbers in the right-hand column are large so, when the different values of $x - x_0$ have a common factor, this is usually taken out as follows.

2

x	f	$\dfrac{x-x_0}{500}$	$f\dfrac{x-x_0}{500}$
750·5	50	−5	−250
1250·5	100	−4	−400
1750·5	173	−3	−519
2250·5	731	−2	−1462
2750·5	3060	−1	−3060
$x_0 = $ 3250·5	6104	0	0
3750·5	4584	1	4584
4250·5	1586	2	3172
	$n=\overline{16388}$		$\sum f\dfrac{x-x_0}{500}=\overline{\overline{2065}}$

$$\bar{x} = x_0 + \frac{1}{n}\sum f(x-x_0) \qquad \textbf{(5a)}$$

$$= 3250\cdot5 + \frac{500 \times 2065}{16\,388}$$

$$= 3250\cdot5 + 63\cdot00$$

$$\therefore \bar{x} = 3314 \text{ g}$$

Note that we are using exactly the same formula as before but we must remember to replace whatever factor has been taken out from the $(x-x_0)$'s: in the right-hand column we have found

$$\sum f\frac{x-x_0}{500}$$

so we multiply 2065 by 500 to find the value of $\sum f(x-x_0)$.

Exercise 2e

Note. The best statistics on which to perform calculations are your own. With cooperation, it is easy to obtain frequency distributions for bodily measurements, pulse and breathing rates, time of going to bed or arriving at school, time taken to get to school, distance from school, number of books read per year, number of cousins, etc. Treat these distributions in the same way as those given below.

1. What are the mid-points of the following intervals, both ends being inclusive?

(i) 70 in.–71 in., when the variate is recorded correct to the nearest $\frac{1}{4}$ in.?

(ii) 7·5 sec–8·0 sec, when the variate is recorded in completed tenths of a second?

2. (For discussion.) How would you record and group the following variates?

(i) Ages of the population of Great Britain.

(ii) The time taken by members of your school to run 100 yd.

(iii) The weights of men joining the army.

(iv) The span of people of the same age and sex as yourself.

3. Find the frequency distribution of ages (as given by the school list) of pupils in your school. (What intervals would be appropriate?) Calculate the mean age of pupils in the school. Alternatively calculate the mean age of the following distribution of ages of grammar school boys in the lower sixths of 13 schools. Ages are given in years and completed months.

Age	15.0 & 15.1	15.2 & 15.3	15.4 & 15.5	15.6 & 15.7	15.8 & 15.9	15.10 & 15.11	16.0 & 16.1	16.2 & 16.3
Frequency	6	8	22	14	22	31	45	71

	16.4 & 16.5	16.6 & 16.7	16.8 & 16.9	16.10 & 16.11	17.0 & 17.1	17.2 & 17.3	17.4 & 17.5	Total
	69	67	72	97	37	6	9	576

4. L. *The production of butter fat during 7 consecutive days was recorded for 219 cows. Calculate the mean of the following distribution. (H. L. Rietz, *Biometrika* 7, 106.)

Butter fat (lb)	7–	8–	9–	10–	11–	12–	13–	14–	15–	16–
Frequency	8	62	59	38	33	10	5	1	2	1

5. L. *Calculate the mean length of worms given in the following distribution. (R. Pearl, and W. W. Fuller, *Biometrika* 4, 217.)

Length (cm)	10–	12·5–	15–	17·5–	20–	22·5–	25–	27·5–	30–
Frequency	7	50	75	153	137	55	9	1	0

* You are advised to leave space for a column of working on the right and for further working below.

6. L. *Find the mean population of parliamentary constituencies which were boroughs in 1960 from the following frequency distribution. (The Registrar General's *Statistical review of England and Wales*, 1961.)

Population	30000–	35000–	40000–	45000–	50000–	55000–
Frequency	1	11	12	46	71	66

	60000–	65000–	70000–	75000–	80000–	Total
	40	26	22	1	3	299

7. L. 260 No. $2\frac{1}{2}$ cans of tomatoes were drained and the contents weighed. The following frequency distribution was obtained; calculate its mean. (E. L. Grant, *Statistical quality control*.)

Weight (oz)	15·5	16·0	16·5	17·0	17·5	18·0	18·5	19·0	19·5	20·0
Frequency	1	0	1	0	2	0	2	7	12	24

20·5	21·0	21·5	22·0	22·5	23·0	23·5	24·0	24·5	25·0	25·5
26	41	33	34	31	14	14	9	6	2	1

8. L. *The frequency distribution below was obtained from 200 measurements of the rate of steam production in a boiler (units: tons per hour). Calculate the mean rate. (A. Hald, *Statistical theory with engineering applications*.)

Rate (t/h)	32·25	32·45	32·65	32·85	33·05	33·25	33·45
Frequency	2	2	1	5	7	6	10

33·65	33·85	34·05	34·25	34·45	34·65	34·85	35·05
7	15	13	25	17	23	21	10

	35·25	35·45	35·65	35·85	36·05	36·25	36·45	36·65
	14	9	4	3	4	0	1	1

* You are advised to leave space for a column of working on the right and for further working below.

9. L. *The heights of 2517 men requiring life insurance were distributed as follows. Calculate the mean of the distribution.

Height (in)	60·5	61·5	62·5	63·5	64·5	65·5	66·5	67·5	68·5
Frequency	0	3	10	26	53	106	195	301	381

69·5	70·5	71·5	72·5	73·5	74·5	75·5	76·5	77·5	78·5
369	383	269	186	137	54	26	15	2	1

(D. M. Lyon, *Clinical Journal*, 71, 241.)

10. Suppose x_0 had been taken to be 2750·5 in the calculation on page 24, what would have been the corresponding value of

$$\Sigma f \frac{x - x_0}{500} \, ?$$

(There is no need to repeat the calculation.)

11. A and B take arbitrary origins x_0 and x_0' to calculate the mean of a frequency distribution. What will be the difference between the values of $\Sigma f(x - x_0)$ which they (should) obtain?

12. L. In an epidemic of Rubella in 1962 the following distributions of ages were obtained. Calculate and compare the mean ages of male and female cases. (J. Fry, J. B. Dillane, and L. Kay, *British Medical Journal*, 29 Sept. 1962, 833.)

Age	0–	1–	5–	10–	15–	20–	30–	40–	50–	60–	Total
No. of males	2	20	71	37	10	21	4	8	1	0	174
No. of females	4	17	65	40	15	20	16	4	0	0	181

13. L. The scores on a reasoning test of 64 boys in the lower sixth form of a grammar school were as follows:

```
23  23  20  18  26   2  43  15  26  25   42  19  21  25  19    2  10  20  14   8
36  59  31  25  45   2  27  33  29  33   52  30  59  18  17   17  19  17  19  38
11  55  15  20  20   8  43   6  12  51   25  12  39  27  41   40  48  25  14  16
20  14  17  13
```

Find the frequency distribution of these marks taking the intervals of successive groups to be 0–4, 5–9, 10–14, etc. Compare the values obtained for the mean (i) from the original marks using **(5)** (or **(4)** with a machine), (ii) from the frequency distribution using **(5a)**.

CHAPTER 3

Standard deviation

3.1. Expectant mothers visiting the doctor are usually told early in pregnancy the date when the baby is due. Such information is obviously helpful but it can be quite misleading and can lead to anxiety if the baby does not arrive on time; in fact only about five per cent arrive on the expected date. This is because the period of gestation is calculated from an *average* length and no allowance is made for factors which may make a particular pregnancy longer or shorter than average. To be fair to the doctors, an expectant mother may well be told that it is quite usual for the baby to arrive up to a fortnight early or a fortnight late—or even more.

The last paragraph illustrates the fact that in any distribution there are individual variations either side of the mean. The question we are trying to answer is, 'How much variation is there?' In other words, we are looking for a measure of this variation. The same phenomenon is also referred to as dispersion, spread, or scatter. The two histograms below provide a graphic illustration of the problem: the total frequencies of the two distributions are the same, and so are the means, but it is clear that the lower one is considerably more dispersed from the mean than the higher.

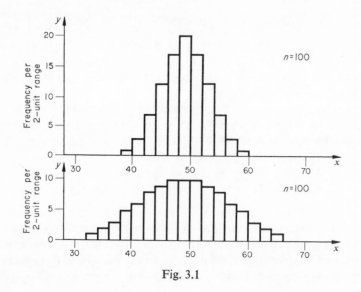

Fig. 3.1

Standards of measurement

3.2. Every measurement is made relative to some standard: a measurement of mass is a comparison with an arbitrary cylinder of platinum defining a kilogramme kept in Paris; a measurement of length is a comparison with the wave length of a certain type of light and even time is defined with reference to the oscillations of a certain kind of atom. All measurements, indeed, are comparisons with arbitrary standards: the standards can be chosen for convenience—what matters is that people who want to compare measurements should use the same standard. You may think that scientists have chosen awkward standards for length, mass and time, but the experts find these the best they can devise at the present time. In the same way, you may think that the statistician's way of measuring dispersion is rather cumbersome, but it, too, is the most satisfactory measure that has been devised for use in mathematical statistics. Other measures of dispersion are used in certain applications of statistics but they will not be used in this book.

The next section introduces the standard deviation by the way the author has found most effective with those having the necessary knowledge of dynamics but, if you are unfamiliar with what is known as the 'radius of gyration' of a rigid body, you are advised to turn straight to §3.4, p. 30.

Radius of gyration

3.3. In §2.4, p. 18, we saw that there was a close analogy between the mean in statistics and the centroid in mechanics. If each value of a variate is represented by a unit mass at the corresponding point on the x-axis, $\bar{x}$ may be thought of either as the mean of the distribution or as the centroid of the masses. Now, we are looking for a measure of dispersion in statistics and it is reasonable to ask ourselves whether we have met any measure of dispersion in mechanics.

Consider a body free to rotate about a fixed axis through its centroid. If we consider it to be made up of elements of mass m at distance r from the axis, its moment of inertia $I = \sum mr^2$. Further if the total mass of the body is M, its radius of gyration

$$k = \sqrt{\frac{\sum mr^2}{M}}$$

Since $Mk^2 = \sum mr^2$, k may be regarded as the radius of a circular ring of equal mass and equal moment of inertia about the axis (which is through the centre of the ring and perpendicular to its plane). Since every point on the ring is equidistant from the axis, k may be regarded as a measure of the dispersion of the mass away from the axis. A few examples are shown in Fig. 3.2; the dispersion of the mass away from the axis increases from left to right.

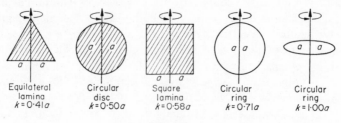

Fig. 3.2

To return to statistics, this suggests that we may find a measure of dispersion by analogy with the radius of gyration. We replace m by f, r by $x - \bar{x}$ (since we took the axis through the centroid), and M by n. Thus to

$$M = \sum m \qquad \text{corresponds} \qquad n = \sum f$$

to

$$\bar{x} = \frac{\sum mx}{M} \qquad \text{corresponds} \qquad \bar{x} = \frac{\sum fx}{n}$$

and to

$$k = \sqrt{\frac{\sum mr^2}{M}} \qquad \text{corresponds} \qquad s = \sqrt{\frac{\sum f(x - \bar{x})^2}{n}}$$

So the *standard deviation s* is defined by

$$s = \sqrt{\frac{\sum f(x - \bar{x})^2}{n}}$$

or, now that we shall not need to use m for mass again,

$$s = \sqrt{\frac{\sum f(x - m)^2}{n}} \tag{7}$$

where m is the mean of the distribution.

Standard deviation

3.4. For those who have not met the radius of gyration, another physical example may be helpful. Most of us use alternating electric current to light our homes and schools; suppose you consider a particular light bulb: what is the average current flowing through it when it is on? The current changes direction 100 times a second, taking alternately positive and negative values, and in the ordinary sense of average the mean current is zero. But quite evidently there *is* a current because it produces light. Now the rate at which the bulb uses energy varies as the *square* of the current, so the physicist finds the average of the square of the current—and then takes the square root of this average to get back to the right units. Thus alternating current is measured by its 'root mean square' value.

The mathematician measures dispersion by a similar device; this measure is called the *standard deviation*; it will be represented by *s*, or in some later work by σ (sigma), and is defined by **(7)** at the end of the last section. In words, it is the *root mean square deviation from the mean*:

The deviation from the mean *m* is $x - m$

The square deviation from the mean is $(x - m)^2$

The mean square deviation from the mean is $\dfrac{\Sigma f(x - m)^2}{n}$

The root mean square deviation from the mean is $\sqrt{\dfrac{\Sigma f(x - m)^2}{n}}$

We square the deviations to get rid of negative signs, then finally we take the square root to get back to the right units. The term 'standard deviation' is aptly chosen, for this measure of dispersion provides a standard against which deviations from the mean may be compared.

Here is a simple, artificial example showing the calculation of the standard deviation from its definition.

Example 1. *Five men have weights* 166, 169, 170, 173, 177 *lb; find the mean and standard deviation of these weights.*

To find the mean, take 170 as arbitrary origin; the deviations from 170 of the weights

$$166, \quad 169, \quad 170, \quad 173, \quad 177$$

are respectively

$$-4, \quad -1, \quad 0, \quad 3, \quad 7$$

Their sum is 5, so the mean of the deviations from 170 is 1 and so the mean weight is 171 lb.

The deviations from the mean are respectively

$$-5, \quad -2, \quad -1, \quad 2, \quad 6$$

their squares are

$$25, \quad 4, \quad 1, \quad 4, \quad 36$$

Their mean square deviation is

$$\frac{25 + 4 + 1 + 4 + 36}{5} = \frac{70}{5} = 14$$

So the standard deviation (which is the root mean square deviation) is $\sqrt{14} \simeq 4 \cdot 12 \, \text{lb}$.

Question 1. Calculate the standard deviation of the following lengths in inches: 2, 3, 6, 6, 8.

It may have occurred to you to question why we need to square the deviations. First, suppose that we add the deviations as they stand in Example 1; we should then obtain

$$-5-2-1+2+6 = 0$$

and, indeed, this will always be so by **(4b)**. Then suppose we ignore the signs of the deviations:

$$5+2+1+2+6 = 16$$

we could then find the mean of these differences—and this would provide a measure of dispersion called the *mean deviation*. However it is not such a satisfactory one for two reasons: (1) the manipulation of the differences from the mean would make theoretical work much more awkward, (2) the mean deviation is a less satisfactory measure of spread when we are taking a sample because, in loose terms, it is likely to deviate from its value in the population as a whole more than the standard deviation would. The reasons for this are involved, so we shall leave the matter there.

Another possible measure of spread is the *range*: the difference between the highest and lowest values of the variate. Although it is easy to calculate, the range suffers from the disadvantage that 'odd' individuals at either end can considerably affect its value. In brief, the standard deviation is chosen out of a number of possible measures of dispersion because: (i) it is based on all the numbers of the distribution and not just a few, (ii) it is easily manipulated by well-known mathematical techniques, (iii) it is least liable to error when samples are taken, (iv) it fits in with other statistical measures called moments being, itself, the second moment about the mean.

Note. (1) The square of the standard deviation is called the *variance*. This is of particular importance in Chapter 10.

(2) For many distributions the range is found in practice to be about six times the standard deviation; examples that illustrate this very approximate relationship will be found later in this chapter and in following ones.

The next example is chosen both because the mean is an integer, which assists calculation, and because the distribution is an example of one which will play an important part in the next chapter.

Example 2. *Find the standard deviation of the ideal frequency distribution of the number of heads obtained when 8 coins are spun together 256 times.*

No. of heads x	0	1	2	3	4	5	6	7	8
Frequency f	1	8	28	56	70	56	28	8	1

From symmetry (calculate it if you wish!) it may be seen that the mean of the distribution $m=4$ heads. The working is tabulated below. The first two columns come from the table above; the headings indicate how the other columns have been calculated.

x	f	$x-m$	$(x-m)^2$	$f(x-m)^2$
0	1	-4	16	16
1	8	-3	9	72
2	28	-2	4	112
3	56	-1	1	56
$m=4$	70	0	0	0
5	56	1	1	56
6	28	2	4	112
7	8	3	9	72
8	1	4	16	16
	256			512

$$n = \Sigma f = 256$$

$$s = \sqrt{\frac{\Sigma f(x-m)^2}{n}} = \sqrt{\frac{512}{256}} = \sqrt{2} = 1\cdot414\ldots$$

(The third column shows the deviations of x from the mean 4; the entries in the fourth column are the squares of those in the third; those in the fifth are the products of corresponding entries in the second and fourth.)

Exercise 3a

1. Six young apple trees produce 4, 6, 10, 11, 13, 16 apples. Find the mean and standard deviation of the number of apples.

2. With the data of Example 2, find the percentage of the frequency distribution for which the variate lies within the ranges: (i) $m-s<x<m+s$, (ii) $m-2s<x<m+2s$, (iii) $m-3s<x<m+3s$.

3. Calculate the standard deviation of the theoretical distribution of the number of heads obtained when 6 coins are spun together 64 times:

No. of heads x	0	1	2	3	4	5	6
Frequency f	1	6	15	20	15	6	1

4. Find the standard deviation of the 'rectangular' distribution below. (It is called rectangular because of the shape of the histogram; approximately rectangular distributions are produced, for example, by the number of people with birthdays in the seven days of the week etc.)

x	0	1	2	3	4	5	6	7	8
f	1	1	1	1	1	1	1	1	1

What would be the effect on the standard deviation of multiplying each frequency by 10?

5. A frequency distribution is given below:

x	0	1	2	3	4
f	81	108	54	12	1

Find the mean square deviations from (i) 2, (ii) 1, (iii) 0. Which of these is the variance of the distribution?

6. In two tests, five pupils A, B, C, D, E scored as follows:

	A	B	C	D	E
First test	9	7	5	3	1
Second test	3	4	5	6	7
Total	12	11	10	9	8

Explain why the pupils' order in the total is the same as their order in the first test. Would the order in the total have been the same if all the marks in the second test had been increased by 10?

7. A number of people take a test and answer all the questions either right or wrong. What can you say about the standard deviations of the distributions of the number of right answers and the number of wrong answers made by those taking part?

8. (For those with a knowledge of the radius of gyration.) For any distribution we shall want to express the mean square deviation from an arbitrary origin in terms of the mean square deviation from the mean (this latter is the variance). Use the analogy with mechanics to find this relationship. (There is a theorem relating the square of the radius of gyration of a rigid body about an axis through the centroid with that about a parallel axis.)

Use of an arbitrary origin

3.5. In practice it is very seldom that the mean of a distribution turns out to be a convenient integer as in the examples of Exercise 3a. We therefore require some means of calculating the standard deviation of a distribution using an arbitrary origin. First let us recall two necessary formulae:

$$\text{the standard deviation } s = \sqrt{\frac{\sum f(x-m)^2}{n}} \tag{7}$$

also we proved in Example 2, Chapter 2, p. 21, that

$$\sum f(x-m) = 0 \tag{4b}$$

Let us see if we can obtain an expression for s^2 using the mean square deviation from x_0 instead of from m. The mean square deviation from x_0 is

$$\frac{\sum f(x-x_0)^2}{n} \tag{i}$$

Now, to bring in s we must use the deviations from m, so we write the numerator of (i) as

$$\sum f\{(x-m)+(m-x_0)\}^2$$

Expanding the braces (i.e. 'curly brackets') as $(a+b)^2$, this becomes

$$\sum f\{(x-m)^2+2(x-m)(m-x_0)+(m-x_0)^2\}$$
$$= \sum f(x-m)^2+2\sum f(x-m)(m-x_0)+\sum f(m-x_0)^2 \tag{ii}$$

The last term of (ii) contains a constant factor $(m-x_0)^2$ which we can take outside the summation sign giving $(m-x_0)^2 \sum f=(m-x_0)^2 n$. Similarly the middle term of (ii) may be written $2(m-x_0) \sum f(x-m)=0$ (by **(4b)**). Hence (ii) may be written

$$\sum f(x-m)^2+n(m-x_0)^2$$

$$\therefore \frac{\sum f(x-x_0)^2}{n} = \frac{\sum f(x-m)^2}{n}+(m-x_0)^2$$

$$\therefore \frac{\sum f(x-x_0)^2}{n} = s^2+(m-x_0)^2 \tag{iii}$$

$$\therefore s^2 = \frac{\sum f(x-x_0)^2}{n}-(m-x_0)^2 \tag{8}$$

Note. (1) $(m-x_0)^2$ can be thought of as a 'correction' to be made to the mean square deviation due to having taken deviations from x_0 instead of from m.

(2) Taking different arbitrary origins, we obtain different mean square deviations; since $(m-x_0)^2 \geqslant 0$, it may be seen from (iii) that the mean square deviation is least when $x_0 = m$, in which case the mean square deviation is s^2.

(3) Those who have access to a calculating machine may sometimes find it useful to take the origin as 'arbitrary origin'. Substituting $x_0 = 0$ in **(8)**,

$$s^2 = \frac{\Sigma fx^2}{n} - m^2 \qquad (9)$$

Example 3. *If 5 seeds of a certain flower are raised, 0, 1, 2, 3, 4, or 5 plants with white flowers may be obtained. The theoretical distribution of the number of white-flowered plants when the experiment is repeated 1024 times is as follows:*

No. of plants x	0	1	2	3	4	5
Frequency f	243	405	270	90	15	1

Find the standard deviation of the distribution. How many values of the variate lie outside the range $m-3s < x < m+3s$?

x	f	$x-x_0$	$f(x-x_0)$	$f(x-x_0)^2$
0	243	-1	-243	243
$x_0 = 1$	405	0	0	0
2	270	1	270	270
3	90	2	180	360
4	15	3	45	135
5	1	4	4	16
	1024		256	1024

(The entries in the fifth column are most easily found by multiplying the corresponding numbers in the third and fourth columns.)

$$m - x_0 = \frac{\Sigma f(x-x_0)}{n} \qquad \text{(from (5a))}$$

$$= \frac{256}{1024} = \frac{1}{4}$$

$$\frac{\Sigma f(x-x_0)^2}{n} = \frac{1024}{1024} = 1$$

$$s^2 = \frac{\sum f(x-x_0)^2}{n} - (m-x_0)^2 \tag{8}$$

$$= 1-(\tfrac{1}{4})^2 = \tfrac{15}{16}$$

$$\therefore s = \tfrac{1}{4}\sqrt{15} \simeq 0\cdot968$$

Further

$$m = x_0 + \tfrac{1}{4} = 1\tfrac{1}{4}$$

The range

$$m-3s < x < m+3s$$

is therefore

$$1\cdot25 - 3\times0\cdot968 < x < 1\cdot25 + 3\times0\cdot968$$

i.e.

$$-1\cdot654 < x < 4\cdot154$$

From this it may be seen that only one value of the variate lies outside this range, namely that given by $x=5$.

Exercise 3b

1. Prove the formula **(9)** from first principles (along the lines of §3.5).

2. L. Find the standard deviation of the number of peas per pod in the distribution of Exercise 2d, No. 3, p. 21.

3. L. Find the standard deviation of the number of dice scoring 5 or 6 in the distribution of Exercise 2d, No. 4, p. 21.

4. Find the percentages of the distributions in Nos. 2 and 3 which lie within 1, 2 and 3 standard deviations of the means.

Grouped frequency distributions

3.6. In §2.6, Chapter 2, p. 21, we estimated the mean of a continuous variable by calculating with the mid-value of the weight in each of the given intervals. We shall follow the same procedure in estimating the standard deviation and again we introduce a small error by making this approximation; in the case of the standard deviation, the saving of time produced by this method is so great that the reader will probably consider a certain inaccuracy to be not very important. You may, however, like to know that under certain conditions corrections can be made for the grouping of the data; for these the reader is advised to consult a more comprehensive book under the heading 'Sheppard's corrections'.

Example 4. *Find the mean and standard deviation of the age of the male Malay population of the Cocos Islands on* 31 *December* 1947 *given in* *the first and third columns of the table below.* (T. E. Smith, *Population Studies*, XIV (1960), 102.)

Age (yr)	Mid-value x	Frequency f	$\dfrac{x-x_0}{5}$	$f\dfrac{x-x_0}{5}$	$f\left(\dfrac{x-x_0}{5}\right)^2$
Under 5	2·5	186	−3	−558	1674
5–9	7·5	145	−2	−290	580
10–14	12·5	102	−1	−102	102
15–19	$x_0 = 17\cdot5$	110	0	0	0
20–24	22·5	80	1	80	80
25–29	27·5	74	2	148	296
30–34	32·5	50	3	150	450
35–39	37·5	29	4	116	464
40–44	42·5	35	5	175	875
45–49	47·5	27	6	162	972
50–54	52·5	16	7	112	784
55–59	57·5	17	8	136	1088
60–64	62·5	10	9	90	810
65–69	67·5	11	10	110	1100
70 & over	72·5	12	11	132	1452
		904		461	10 727

From this working we see that:

$$n = 904$$

$$\Sigma f(x-x_0) = 5 \times \Sigma f\frac{x-x_0}{5} = 5 \times 461 = 2305$$

$$\Sigma f(x-x_0)^2 = 25 \times \Sigma f\left(\frac{x-x_0}{5}\right)^2 = 25 \times 10\,727 = 268\,175$$

Now
$$m = x_0 + \frac{1}{n}\sum f(x-x_0) \tag{5a}$$

$$\therefore m = 17\cdot5 + \tfrac{2305}{904} = 17\cdot5 + 2\cdot550$$

$$\therefore m = 20\cdot05 \text{ yr}$$

Further
$$s^2 = \frac{1}{n}\sum f(x-x_0)^2 - (m-x_0)^2 \tag{8}$$

$$= \tfrac{268\,175}{904} - \left(\tfrac{2305}{904}\right)^2$$

$$= 296\cdot65 - 6\cdot50 = 290\cdot15$$

$$\therefore s = 17\cdot0 \text{ yr}$$

Note that the expression $m - x_0$ whose square is needed in the calculation of s appears in the calculation of m. Here it is $\frac{2305}{904} = 2\cdot550$. An alternative way of calculating s is to work directly from the sum of the columns:

$$s^2 = 25 \times \left\{ \frac{10\,727}{904} - \left(\frac{461}{904}\right)^2 \right\}$$

To show that this is equivalent to what we had before, write the right-hand side as

$$\frac{10\,727 \times 25}{904} - \left(\frac{461 \times 5}{904}\right)^2 = \frac{268\,175}{904} - \left(\frac{2305}{904}\right)^2$$

In the following exercise, only do enough of the numerical calculations to give yourself confidence in the method—a larger number of examples are provided than most people will need.

Exercise 3c

1. Find the mean and standard deviation of the ages of 576 boys in the lower sixths of 13 maintained grammar schools. The ages are given in years and months and are the mid-value of the intervals.

Age	15.1	15.3	15.5	15.7	15.9	15.11	16.1
Frequency	6	8	22	14	22	31	45

	16.3	16.5	16.7	16.9	16.11	17.1	17.3	17.5	Total
	71	69	67	72	97	37	6	9	576

2. Find the standard deviations of the frequency distributions of Nos. 4, 5, 6, 7, 8, 9 of Exercise 2e, p. 24. Draw the histograms and on each mark off distances of 1, 2, 3 standard deviations either side of the mean.

3. A standard deviation is calculated by two people using different arbitrary origins x_0, x_0'. Find in terms of n, m, x_0, x_0' the difference between their sums of squares, namely $\sum f(x - x_0)^2 - \sum f(x - x_0')^2$.

4. If the frequencies in Example 4 were doubled, what would be the effect on the standard deviation?

5. Compare the standard deviation of the distribution of Exercise 2e, No. 13 obtained from the original marks with the estimate obtained from the frequency distribution in which the marks are grouped as suggested. (The labour of the former calculation can be reduced by cooperative working in finding the sum of square deviations from an arbitrary origin; alternatively a calculating machine would ease the labour.)

6. Prove the formula (**8**) by writing

$$\sum \frac{f(x-m)^2}{n} = \sum \frac{f\{(x-x_0)+(x_0-m)\}^2}{n}$$

(Compare the proof in §3.5, p. 35).

7. T. A check on the sums involved in calculating a mean and standard deviation can be made as follows. Suppose that the difference between successive mid-values is c (in Example 4 it was 5), then

$$\sum f + 2 \sum f \frac{x-x_0}{c} + \sum f\left(\frac{x-x_0}{c}\right)^2 \equiv \sum f\left(\frac{x-x_0}{c}+1\right)^2$$

(In Example 4, $904 + 2 \times 461 + 10727 = 12553$.)

Prove the identity above (it may help to write $u = (x-x_0)/c$) and apply it to Example 3, p. 36. (The right-hand side of the identity has to be calculated independently; here it is

$$243 \times 0 + 405 \times 1 + 270 \times 4 + 90 \times 9 + 15 \times 16 + 1 \times 25.)$$

If only the mean is being calculated, what identity could provide a check on the working?

CHAPTER 4

Probability distributions

4.1. We have seen something of probability in Chapter 1 and have spent some time on frequency distributions in Chapters 2 and 3; in this chapter we bring the two strands together and introduce some of the simpler probability distributions. Apart from having interest and applications in their own right, these distributions provide the basis for tests of statistical significance, which will occupy most of the subsequent parts of the book.

Rectangular distribution

4.2. The simplest probability distribution is the rectangular distribution; in this the probability is uniform throughout the range of the variate. This is by no means artificial or of only academic interest: for instance we should hope that children born at different times of the year would have equal chances in their education—but there is evidence to show that this may not be so. However, for the study of the distributions themselves, it is clearer to take artificial examples for which the probability is not in dispute. For instance, we may suppose that the probability distribution of the final digit of a number chosen at random from a telephone directory is as follows.

Final digit x	0	1	2	3	4	5	6	7	8	9
Probability P	0·1	0·1	0·1	0·1	0·1	0·1	0·1	0·1	0·1	0·1

We may draw a histogram of this distribution which makes it clear why the distribution is described as 'rectangular'.

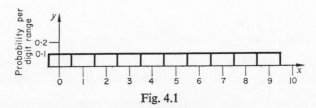

Fig. 4.1

Note. (1) The probabilities are represented by areas.
(2) The total area is 1.

Exercise 4a

1. Which of the following distributions are rectangular?

(i) The first digit of a number drawn at random from a telephone directory.

(ii) The score when a die is thrown.

(iii) The score when two dice are thrown.

(iv) The month that a British baby is born in.

2. Suggest, and discuss, other distributions that may be rectangular.

Symmetrical binomial distribution

4.3. This distribution arises whenever we want to test the hypothesis that the chances of an event are 'fifty-fifty' but it will also lead us on to the very important 'normal distribution'. The simplest illustration of the symmetrical binomial distribution is provided by tossing a coin.

We have said that a coin is equally likely to turn up 'heads' and 'tails'. Now we shall discuss what might happen if this experiment is repeated a number of times. Let us examine all the possible results of 4 trials. 'H' and 'T' will stand for the occurrence of a head and a tail respectively. At any stage, every combination of results can be followed by either H or T—this is shown diagrammatically below.

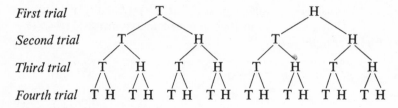

After the first trial the probabilities are clearly:

No. of heads x	0	1
Probability P	$\frac{1}{2}$	$\frac{1}{2}$

After the second trial the possibilities are TT, TH, HT, HH. If the order in which the heads are obtained is ignored, the probability distribution is:

No. of heads x	0	1	2
Probability P	$\frac{1}{4}$	$\frac{1}{2}$	$\frac{1}{4}$

You can trace out on the diagram above the possibilities arising after the third trial. The frequencies of 0, 1, 2, 3 heads shown on it are 1, 3, 3, 1 respectively, giving the following probability distribution.

No. of heads x	0	1	2	3
Probability P	$\frac{1}{8}$	$\frac{3}{8}$	$\frac{3}{8}$	$\frac{1}{8}$

After four trials we obtain:

No. of heads x	0	1	2	3	4
Probability P	$\frac{1}{16}$	$\frac{4}{16}$	$\frac{6}{16}$	$\frac{4}{16}$	$\frac{1}{16}$

We could go on in this way but it is more instructive to use our knowledge of probability to obtain the distribution for 5 trials. The probability of a head $p=\frac{1}{2}$ and the probability of a tail $q=\frac{1}{2}$.

Case 1. No head. Each trial must give a tail; the events are independent and so, by the generalisation of **(3)**, the probability is $\frac{1}{2}\times\frac{1}{2}\times\frac{1}{2}\times\frac{1}{2}\times\frac{1}{2}=\frac{1}{32}$.

Case 2. One head. The probability of obtaining *in this order* HTTTT is $\frac{1}{2}\times\frac{1}{2}\times\frac{1}{2}\times\frac{1}{2}\times\frac{1}{2}=\frac{1}{32}$. But the head may come in any of 5 places which are mutually exclusive, so by the generalisation of **(2)**, the probability of one head is $\frac{5}{32}$.

Case 3. Two heads. The probability of obtaining *in this order* HHTTT is $\frac{1}{2}\times\frac{1}{2}\times\frac{1}{2}\times\frac{1}{2}\times\frac{1}{2}=\frac{1}{32}$. But two H's and three T's may be arranged in $\dfrac{5!}{2!\,3!}$ distinct orders (see below) so the probability of two heads is $\dfrac{5!}{2!\,3!}\cdot\dfrac{1}{32}=\dfrac{10}{32}$.

We may fill in the remaining entries in the distribution by symmetry:

No. of heads x	0	1	2	3	4	5
Probability P	$\frac{1}{32}$	$\frac{5}{32}$	$\frac{10}{32}$	$\frac{10}{32}$	$\frac{5}{32}$	$\frac{1}{32}$

(*To find the arrangements of* 2 *H's and* 3 *T's.* If we give the letters suffixes H_1, H_2, T_1, T_2, T_3, we have 5 distinct letters which can be arranged in 5! ways (the first can be any one of 5; for each of these the second can be any one of four, giving 5×4 ways of selecting the first two; then there will be $5\times4\times3$ ways of selecting the first three, and so on, giving $5\times4\times3\times2\times1$ ways of arranging the five letters.) But in each of these 5! ways the H's may be arranged in 2! ways and the T's may be arranged in 3! ways, so that each arrangement of the H's and T's is repeated $2!\times3!$ times. Hence, if we drop the suffixes, there are only $5!/(2!3!)$ distinguishable arrangements of the H's and T's.)

Exercise 4b

1. Check that, in each of the four probability distributions above, the sum of the probabilities is 1. Sketch the four histograms; what is the area under each?

2. Find the probability distribution of the number of heads obtained in six spins of a coin.

3. Assuming the probability of a piglet being male to be $\frac{1}{2}$, find the probability distribution of the number of male piglets in litters of eight.

4. Show that $n-r$ like objects of one kind and r like objects of another may be arranged in order in $\dfrac{n!}{(n-r)!\,r!}$ ways. Hence find the probability distribution of the number of heads obtained in n trials with a coin.

5. Find the probabilities of obtaining (i) 4, (ii) 5, (iii) 6 heads, when 10 coins are spun. Verify that one is more likely to get either 4 or 6 than exactly 5 heads.

General binomial distribution

4.4. In this section we shall speak of 'events' in general but, to fix your ideas on a particular example, it may be helpful to think of an event as a throw of a die. We shall find the probability distribution of the number of *successes* (you may think of a success as throwing a six) in *n trials* (which may be thought of as throws). Let the probability of a success in any trial be p and the probability of a failure (i.e. not obtaining a success) be q so that $p+q=1$ **(1)**.

Case 1. No success. The probability of not obtaining a success in any particular trial is q. The results of the n trials are independent so the probability of no success is q^n.

Case 2. One success. Suppose the first $n-1$ trials are failures and the remaining one is a success. Since the trials are independent, the probability of this result is $q^{n-1}p$. But the success might come in any one of n positions; these are mutually exclusive, so the probability of one success is $nq^{n-1}p$.

Case 3. $n-r$ failures, r successes. Suppose that $n-r$ failures are followed by r successes. The probability of this is $q^{n-r}p^r$ since the events are independent. Now the $n-r$ failures and r successes may be arranged in

$\dfrac{n!}{(n-r)!\,r!}$ ways which are mutually exclusive. So the probability of $n-r$ failures and r successes is $\dfrac{n!}{(n-r)!\,r!}\,q^{n-r}p^r$.

Case 4. n successes. The probability is p^n since the events are independent.

The reader familiar with the binomial theorem will see that the probability distribution is made up of the terms of the expansion of $(q+p)^n$.

No. of successes x	0	1	...	r	...	n
Probability P	q^n	$nq^{n-1}p$	...	$\dfrac{n!}{(n-r)!\,r!}\,q^{n-r}p^r$	...	p^n

Question 1. Show that the area under the histogram for this distribution is 1.

Note particularly the condition which has been assumed, namely that the probability of a success is the *same at each trial*. If we draw cards at random from a pack of playing cards, the card must be replaced after each trial, otherwise the binomial distribution is not applicable. Sometimes, however, we can obtain an approximate result using the distribution; this is done in the next example.

Example 1. *If 10 per cent of a large consignment of eggs are bad, what is the probability distribution of the number of bad eggs in a box of half a dozen chosen at random?*

Since the consignment of eggs is large, the selection of an egg, whether good or bad, will leave the probability very nearly the same so we can take the probability of any selected egg being bad to be $p=0\cdot1$. Then $q=0\cdot9$, where q is the probability of the egg not being bad.

The binomial distribution for 6 trials is:

No. of successes x	0	1	2	3	4	5	6
Probability P	q^6	$6q^5p$	$15q^4p^2$	$20q^3p^3$	$15q^2p^4$	$6qp^5$	p^6

substituting $q=0\cdot9$, $p=0\cdot1$ we obtain:

No. of successes x	0	1	2	3	4	5	6
Probability P	$\dfrac{9^6}{10^6}$	$\dfrac{6\times9^5}{10^6}$	$\dfrac{15\times9^4}{10^6}$	$\dfrac{20\times9^3}{10^6}$	$\dfrac{15\times9^2}{10^6}$	$\dfrac{6\times9}{10^6}$	$\dfrac{1}{10^6}$
P to 3 dec. places	0·531	0·354	0·098	0·015	0·001	0·000	0·000

Example 2. *What is the theoretical distribution of the number of sixes obtained when 5 dice are thrown together 7776 times?*

The probability of a six at any throw $p=\frac{1}{6}$ and the probability of not obtaining a six $q=\frac{5}{6}$. The binomial distribution for 5 trials is:

No. of successes x	0	1	2	3	4	5
Probability P	$(\frac{5}{6})^5$	$5(\frac{5}{6})^4(\frac{1}{6})$	$10(\frac{5}{6})^3(\frac{1}{6})^2$	$10(\frac{5}{6})^2(\frac{1}{6})^3$	$5(\frac{5}{6})(\frac{1}{6})^4$	$(\frac{1}{6})^5$

Multiplying the probabilities by 7776 (chosen so that the theoretical frequencies come out exactly) we obtain what may be regarded as an ideal frequency distribution for the number of sixes obtained in 7776 throws of 5 dice:

No. of sixes x	0	1	2	3	4	5
Theoretical frequency f	3125	3125	1250	250	25	1

We could, of course, have multiplied the probabilities by any other convenient number, for instance 100, in which case we would have obtained the percentage of occurrences expected for each value of x.

No of sixes x	0	1	2	3	4	5
Percentage of occurrences	40·2	40·2	16·1	3·2	0·3	0·0

Exercise 4c

1. Find the theoretical frequency distribution for the number of sixes obtained when 3 dice are thrown 216 times.

2. L. Find the probability that, in 100 spins of a coin, exactly 50 heads should be obtained. ($\log_{10} 100! = 157{\cdot}9700$, $\log_{10} 50! = 64{\cdot}4831$.)

3. Find the terms corresponding to $r=35$, 40, 45, 50, 55, 60, 65 in the frequency distribution given by the expansion of $1000(\frac{1}{2}+\frac{1}{2})^{100}$. Plot your results on a graph and draw a smooth curve to pass through them. (The logarithms of 35!, 40!, 45!, 55!, 60!, 65! are respectively, 40·0142, 47·9116, 56·0778, 73·1037, 81·9202, 90·9163.)

4. In a large batch of light bulbs, 3 per cent are defective. If I buy 5 bulbs of this batch, what is the probability that (i) none is defective, (ii) at least one is defective?

5. Take the proportion of cars fitted with safety straps to be 20 per cent. What is the probability that more than half the cars in a pile-up of six are fitted with safety straps?

6. In a certain batch of seed, 10 per cent will not germinate. If 20 seeds are sown, what are the probabilities that (i) less than 2 germinate, (ii) more than 18 germinate?

7. The probability of being dealt the 'best' hand at bridge is $\frac{1}{4}$. In a rubber involving 15 deals, what is the chance that I should get the 'best' hand less than three times?

8. Consider the units digits of the first ten telephone numbers on a page of a telephone directory. Find the theoretical frequency distribution of the number of 3's, 6's or 9's when 100 such groups of digits are examined. Examine 100 pages of a telephone directory and compare the results. (The labour can well be shared with others.)

9. When four dice are thrown together, a 5 or a 6 is counted as a success. What would you expect to be the mean number of successes per trial? Confirm your guess by calculating the mean of the theoretical distribution of the number of successes in 81 trials.

10. M. Show that, if np is integral, then the greatest term of the expansion of $(q+p)^n$ is given by $x=np$.

Mean of a probability distribution

4.5. At this stage it will be useful to introduce a convention about notation: when we are dealing with *theoretical* distributions we shall, in future, use the Greek letters μ and σ for the mean and standard deviation; when we are concerned with *observed* distributions, we shall use the italic forms of the Roman letters m and s respectively. This convention will be extended later on but the distinction will suffice for the moment.

First, let us consider how we can assign a meaning to the mean of a probability distribution. In Example 2, we found the theoretical distribution for the number of sixes in 7776 throws of 5 dice.

No. of sixes x	0	1	2	3	4	5	Total
Theoretical frequency f	3125	3125	1250	250	25	1	7776

The mean of this distribution

$$\mu = \frac{\sum fx}{n} = \frac{3125 \times 0 + 3125 \times 1 + 1250 \times 2 + 250 \times 3 + 25 \times 4 + 1 \times 5}{7776}$$

$$= \frac{0 + 3125 + 2500 + 750 + 100 + 5}{7776}$$

$$= \frac{6480}{7776} = \frac{5}{6}$$

Now the probability distribution of Example 2 can be obtained from the frequency distribution by dividing the frequencies by the total frequency 7776. That is, the probability of any particular number of sixes $P=f/n$. This suggests that we can rewrite the formula for the mean of the frequency distribution in terms of the probabilities.

$$\mu = \frac{\Sigma fx}{n} \tag{4a}$$

but n is constant so this may be written

$$\mu = \sum \frac{f}{n} x$$

But $f/n=P$, where P is the probability of x successes, so that

$$\mu = \Sigma Px \tag{10}$$

We therefore *define* the mean of a probability distribution by formula **(10)**.

Note. (1) μ may be regarded as the average number of successes per trial.

(2) This formula is not applicable, *as it stands*, to distributions of a continuous variable.

Example 3. *Find the mean of the probability distribution*:

x	0	1	2	3	4
P	$(\frac{3}{4})^4$	$4(\frac{3}{4})^3(\frac{1}{4})$	$6(\frac{3}{4})^2(\frac{1}{4})^2$	$4(\frac{3}{4})(\frac{1}{4})^3$	$(\frac{1}{4})^4$

$$\mu = \Sigma Px = \frac{1}{4^4}(81 \times 0 + 108 \times 1 + 54 \times 2 + 12 \times 3 + 1 \times 4)$$
$$= \tfrac{1}{256} \times 256 = 1$$

Therefore the mean of the distribution is 1.

Question 2. What makes the answer come out nicely? (See Exercise 4d, No. 5.)

Exercise 4d

1. Six digits are chosen at random and a 0 or a 5 is counted as a success. The probability distribution of the number of successes is:

No. of successes x	0	1	2	3	4	5	6
Probability P	$(\frac{4}{5})^6$	$6(\frac{4}{5})^5(\frac{1}{5})$	$15(\frac{4}{5})^4(\frac{1}{5})^2$	$20(\frac{4}{5})^3(\frac{1}{5})^3$	$15(\frac{4}{5})^2(\frac{1}{5})^4$	$6(\frac{4}{5})(\frac{1}{5})^5$	$(\frac{1}{5})^6$

Find the mean of this distribution.

2. T. Prove that $\sum P(x-\mu)=0$.

3. If an arbitrary origin x_0 is used to calculate the mean of a probability distribution, what expression should be used to find μ?

4. Show that the mean of the probability distribution given by the terms of the binomial expansion of $(\frac{1}{2}+\frac{1}{2})^n$ is $\frac{1}{2}n$. (*Hint*: Pair values of x with the same values of P.)

5. L. Find the means of the following probability distributions. (Remember that $q+p=1$.)

(i) x	0	1
P	q	p

(ii) x	0	1	2
P	q^2	$2qp$	p^2

(iii) x	0	1	2	3
P	q^3	$3q^2 p$	$3qp^2$	p^3

What do you expect to be the mean of the distribution:

x	0	1	2	3	4
P	q^4	$4q^3 p$	$6q^2 p^2$	$4qp^3$	p^4

Check your conjecture by algebra.

6. T. Show that the mean of the binomial distribution given by the terms of the expansion of $(q+p)^n$

$$\mu = np \qquad (11)$$

(*Hint*: There is a factor of $(q+p)^{n-1}$ in the expression for $\sum Px$.)

7. If I throw a die until I get a six, how many throws shall I need to make, on the average?

8. M. A roulette ball can stop on a red or a black number with equal probability; find the probability distribution of the lengths of runs of the same colour. Also, find the mean and standard deviation of the distribution.

9. M.T. Consider the binomial distribution given by $(q+p)^n$, when p is small, n is large and $np=\mu$, which is finite.

(i) Show that $q^n \to e^{-\mu}$ as $n \to \infty$. (*Hint*: $[1-(\mu/n)]^n \to e^{-\mu}$ as $n \to \infty$.)

(ii) Show that the first terms of the distribution may be written

$$e^{-\mu}\left(1+\mu+\frac{\mu^2}{2!}+\frac{\mu^3}{3!}+\ldots\right)$$

if terms in $1/n$ may be neglected.

(iii) Find the mean of the distribution given by the infinite series in (ii). This distribution was given by Poisson in 1837.

Standard deviation of a probability distribution

4.6. In the last section we took the formula $\mu = \dfrac{\sum fx}{n}$ for the mean of a frequency distribution and rewrote it in the form $\mu = \sum Px$, **(10)**, where $P = f/n$. We shall now carry out the equivalent process to find a formula suitable for the standard deviation of a probability distribution.

For a frequency distribution, the standard deviation is given by

$$s = \sqrt{\frac{\sum f(x-m)^2}{n}} \tag{7}$$

for an observed distribution or by

$$\sigma = \sqrt{\frac{\sum f(x-\mu)^2}{n}}$$

for a theoretical distribution.

Now n is a constant, so we may rewrite this as

$$\sigma = \sqrt{\left\{\sum \frac{f}{n}(x-\mu)^2\right\}}$$
$$= \sqrt{\{\sum P(x-\mu)^2\}}$$

We therefore *define* the standard deviation of a probability distribution by

$$\boldsymbol{\sigma = \sqrt{\{\Sigma\, P(x-\mu)^2\}}} \tag{12}$$

For purposes of calculation, it may be easier to find $\sum Px^2$, and in this case we may write **(12)** as

$$\sigma^2 = \sum P(x^2 - 2x\mu + \mu^2)$$
$$= \sum Px^2 - 2\sum Px\mu + \sum P\mu^2$$

But μ is a constant, so $\sum Px\mu = \mu \sum Px$; now $\sum Px = \mu$ by **(10)**, hence $\sum Px\mu = \mu^2$. Further, $\sum P\mu^2 = \mu^2 \sum P = \mu^2$, since the sum of the probabilities $\sum P = 1$. Hence

$$\sigma^2 = \sum Px^2 - 2\mu^2 + \mu^2$$
$$\therefore \boldsymbol{\sigma^2 = \Sigma\, Px^2 - \mu^2} \tag{13}$$

Example 4. *When 5 coins are spun, the probability distribution of the number of heads is*:

No. of heads x	0	1	2	3	4	5
Probability P	$\dfrac{1}{2^5}$	$\dfrac{5}{2^5}$	$\dfrac{10}{2^5}$	$\dfrac{10}{2^5}$	$\dfrac{5}{2^5}$	$\dfrac{1}{2^5}$

Find the standard deviation of this distribution.

$$\sigma^2 = \sum Px^2 - \mu^2 \tag{13}$$

From symmetry $\mu = 2\frac{1}{2}$.

$$\sum Px^2 = \frac{1}{2^5}(1 \times 0^2 + 5 \times 1^2 + 10 \times 2^2 + 10 \times 3^2 + 5 \times 4^2 + 1 \times 5^2)$$

$$= \tfrac{1}{32}(5 + 40 + 90 + 80 + 25) = \tfrac{240}{32}$$

$$\therefore \sigma^2 = \tfrac{240}{32} - (\tfrac{5}{2})^2 = \tfrac{5}{4}$$

$$\therefore \sigma = \tfrac{1}{2}\sqrt{5} \simeq 1 \cdot 12.$$

Exercise 4e

1. Find the standard deviation of the symmetrical binomial distribution for $n = 6$.

2. Three dice are thrown; find the standard deviation of the probability distribution for the number of sixes obtained.

3. Find the standard deviations of the four distributions in Exercise 4d, No. 5 (p. 49). Remember that $\mu = np$ **(11)** and that $q + p = 1$ **(1)**. Hint for (iv): $\sum Px^2$ may be expressed as $4qp(q+p)^2 + (4p)^2(q+p)^2$.

4. т. Show that the standard deviation of the binomial probability distribution given by the terms of the expansion of $(q+p)^n$ is

$$\sigma = \sqrt{(npq)} \tag{14}$$

(*Hints*: Remember that $\mu = np$ and that $q + p = 1$; $\sum Px^2$ may be expressed as $nqp(q+p)^{n-2} + (np)^2(q+p)^{n-2}$.)

5. If an arbitrary origin x_0 is used to calculate the standard deviation of a probability distribution, what formula should be used to find σ?

6. Find the standard deviation of the probability distribution of the number of throws of a die before a six is obtained.

7. Find the standard deviation of the Poisson distribution given in Exercise 4d, No. 9 (ii) (p. 49).

8. The numbers from 1 to n are drawn at random; what is the standard deviation of the probability distribution of these integers?

The binomial distribution for large n

4.7. In this section we shall compare the histograms corresponding to various binomial distributions. To begin with we shall restrict ourselves to symmetrical distributions, i.e. those which are given by the expansion of $(\frac{1}{2} + \frac{1}{2})^n$.

Now the larger values of n will give a greater range of values on the x-axis. We shall therefore scale them down for comparison. Fortunately we have in the standard deviation a convenient means of doing this. But if we reduce the scale on the x-axis we must increase it on the y-axis *so as to maintain an area of* 1 *under the histogram*. The process is shown for $n=9$ by way of illustration.

x	0	1	2	3	4	5	6	7	8	9
P	$\dfrac{1}{2^9}$	$\dfrac{9}{2^9}$	$\dfrac{36}{2^9}$	$\dfrac{84}{2^9}$	$\dfrac{126}{2^9}$	$\dfrac{126}{2^9}$	$\dfrac{84}{2^9}$	$\dfrac{36}{2^9}$	$\dfrac{9}{2^9}$	$\dfrac{1}{2^9}$

$$\sigma = \sqrt{(npq)} = \sqrt{(9 \times \tfrac{1}{2} \times \tfrac{1}{2})} = 1\tfrac{1}{2} \qquad \text{(by (14))}$$

Take a new origin at the mean $\mu = 4\tfrac{1}{2}$ and let $X = \dfrac{x - 4\tfrac{1}{2}}{1\tfrac{1}{2}}$, then corresponding values of x, X are given below:

x	0	1	2	3	4	5	6	7	8	9
X	-3	$-2\tfrac{1}{3}$	$-1\tfrac{2}{3}$	-1	$-\tfrac{1}{3}$	$\tfrac{1}{3}$	1	$1\tfrac{2}{3}$	$2\tfrac{1}{3}$	3

Since we have reduced the scale by a factor of $1\tfrac{1}{2}$ on the x-axis, we increase it by a factor of $1\tfrac{1}{2}$ on the y-axis so that our modified distribution becomes:

x	0	1	2	3	4	5	6	7	8	9
X	-3	$-2\tfrac{1}{3}$	$-1\tfrac{2}{3}$	-1	$-\tfrac{1}{3}$	$\tfrac{1}{3}$	1	$1\tfrac{2}{3}$	$2\tfrac{1}{3}$	3
Y	$\dfrac{3}{2^{10}}$	$\dfrac{27}{2^{10}}$	$\dfrac{108}{2^{10}}$	$\dfrac{252}{2^{10}}$	$\dfrac{378}{2^{10}}$	$\dfrac{378}{2^{10}}$	$\dfrac{252}{2^{10}}$	$\dfrac{108}{2^{10}}$	$\dfrac{27}{2^{10}}$	$\dfrac{3}{2^{10}}$

In Fig. 4.2 we show the histogram before and after this scaling has been done.

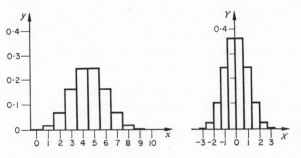

Fig. 4.2

To carry out the same procedure for large values of n is a tedious job without a calculating machine, but this has been done and the results are shown in Fig. 4.3.

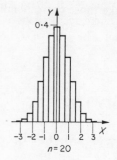
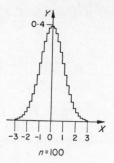

Fig. 4.3

You may notice that the modified histograms have approximately the same height at the centre and spread, as far as can be seen, (some values are too small to be shown on the figure) over much the same range of values of x. As n tends to infinity it seems likely that the modified histogram will approach nearer and nearer to some curve. The likeness would be even closer if we were to join the mid-points of the tops of adjacent rectangles; in this case we should expect the gradients of these lines to approximate to the gradient of the limiting curve. This being so, we may hope to form a differential equation for the curve by considering the gradient of such a line. If you have not met differential equations, or find the mathematics heavy going, you are advised to skip to §4.9.

The limit of the binomial distribution

4.8. Now consider the general case of the symmetrical binomial distribution $(\frac{1}{2}+\frac{1}{2})^n$. If we change the scale along the axes as in §4.7, $\mu=np=\frac{1}{2}n$, by **(11)**, and $\sigma=\sqrt{(npq)}=\sqrt{(n\times\frac{1}{2}\times\frac{1}{2})}=\frac{1}{2}\sqrt{n}$, by **(14)**

$$\therefore X = \frac{x-\mu}{\sigma} = \frac{x-\frac{1}{2}n}{\frac{1}{2}\sqrt{n}} \tag{i}$$

so the distance ΔX between successive values of X is given by

$$\Delta X = \frac{(x+1)-\frac{1}{2}n}{\frac{1}{2}\sqrt{n}} - \frac{x-\frac{1}{2}n}{\frac{1}{2}\sqrt{n}} = \frac{1}{\frac{1}{2}\sqrt{n}}$$

Therefore $\Delta X \to 0$ as $n \to \infty$. Hence the modified histogram appears to become more and more like a curve as $n \to \infty$. Before we jump to conclusions, however, we had better see what happens to the distance ΔY

53

between successive values of Y. We take those corresponding to x and $x+1$. As in the last section, we multiply y by σ to find Y.

$$Y = \frac{n!}{(n-x)!\,x!}\,(\tfrac{1}{2})^n \cdot \tfrac{1}{2}\sqrt{n}$$

$$\therefore \Delta Y = \frac{n!}{(n-x-1)!\,(x+1)!}\,(\tfrac{1}{2})^n \tfrac{1}{2}\sqrt{n} - \frac{n!}{(n-x)!\,x!}\,(\tfrac{1}{2})^n \tfrac{1}{2}\sqrt{n}$$

$$= (\tfrac{1}{2})^n \tfrac{1}{2}\sqrt{n}\,\frac{n!}{(n-x)!\,(x+1)!}\,\{(n-x)-(x+1)\}$$

$$= Y.\frac{n-2x-1}{x+1}$$

But

$$\Delta X = \frac{1}{\tfrac{1}{2}\sqrt{n}}$$

$$\therefore \frac{\Delta Y}{\Delta X} = Y\frac{n-2x-1}{x+1}.\tfrac{1}{2}\sqrt{n}$$

Substituting $x = \tfrac{1}{2}\sqrt{n} . X + \tfrac{1}{2}n$ (from (i)),

$$\frac{\Delta Y}{\Delta X} = Y\frac{n-\sqrt{n}X-n-1}{\tfrac{1}{2}X\sqrt{n}+\tfrac{1}{2}n+1}\tfrac{1}{2}\sqrt{n}$$

$$= Y\frac{-\tfrac{1}{2}nX-\tfrac{1}{2}\sqrt{n}}{\tfrac{1}{2}n+\tfrac{1}{2}X\sqrt{n}+1}$$

Let $n \to \infty$, then $\Delta Y/\Delta X \to dY/dX$, so

$$\frac{dY}{dX} = -XY$$

Separating the variables,

$$\int \frac{dY}{Y} = \int -X\,dX$$

$$\therefore \log_e Y = -\tfrac{1}{2}X^2 + \log_e k \qquad (k \text{ const.})$$

$$\therefore \log_e \frac{Y}{k} = -\tfrac{1}{2}X^2$$

$$\therefore Y = k\,e^{-\tfrac{1}{2}X^2}$$

We find, therefore, that the modified binomial histogram approaches a curve of this form as $n \to \infty$. Now the area of the histogram was 1, so k may be determined by finding for what value the area under the curve is 1. It may be shown that this is so when $k = 1/\sqrt{(2\pi)}$; the proof involves double integrals, the method being indicated in Exercise 4j, No. 6, p. 68. Hence the modified binomial histogram approaches the form

$$y = \frac{1}{\sqrt{(2\pi)}} e^{-\frac{1}{2}x^2} \tag{15}$$

as $n \to \infty$. This curve is called the normal curve and was obtained by Demoivre in 1738 but is more generally associated with the names of Gauss and Laplace who discussed its properties in connection with the study of errors.

It was found that a large number of types of measurement were distributed according to this curve, which may explain its name, 'normal'. Probably too much emphasis was placed on this aspect of the curve but it is hard to underestimate its theoretical importance. This will appear to some extent in the chapters on tests of significance but the distribution is of very considerable importance in the derivation of other probability distributions—this however is outside the scope of this book.

Exercise 4f

1. Calculate values of the ordinates and plot the normal curve **(15)** for values of x from -3 to $+3$. (Alternatively use those in No. 2.)

2. M. The ordinates of the normal curve are given for selected values of x below. Use Simpson's rule (given in calculus text books) to verify that the area under the curve is 1, as far as the accuracy of the data allows the check to be made.

x	0	$\pm\frac{1}{2}$	± 1	$\pm 1\frac{1}{2}$	± 2	$\pm 2\frac{1}{2}$	± 3	$\pm 3\frac{1}{2}$	± 4
y	0.3989	0.3521	0.2420	0.1295	0.0540	0.0175	0.0044	0.0009	0.0001

3. T. Show that the general binomial distribution given by $(q+p)^n$ approaches the normal distribution as $n \to \infty$. (The method of §4.8 can be followed with modifications of detail.)

4. M. Find the maximum and points of inflexion of the normal curve **(15)**.

Normal probabilities

4.9. We have seen in §4.8 how the normal curve **(15)** may be obtained from the limit of a binomial histogram (with suitable changes of scale on the axes) as $n \to \infty$. Now the area under the histogram between two values of x is the same as the area under the modified histogram between corresponding values of X (since the changes of scale on the two axes compensate each other), and each represents the probability that the variate should lie between these values. Similarly, the area under the normal curve between two values of the variate represents the probability that the variate should lie between these values.

Example 5. *Find the probability that a variate distributed according to the normal curve* **(15)** *should*: (*i*) *exceed* 2·0, (*ii*) *be less than* −3·0, (*iii*) *lie between* 1·5 *and* 2·5.

(i) From Table A, p. 188, the area under the normal curve from − ∞ to 2. is 0·9772. This is the unshaded area in Fig. 4.4; we require the shaded area. But the total area under the curve is 1, so the area required is 1 − 0·9772 = 0·0228. This, then, is the probability that a normal variate should exceed 2.

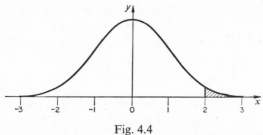

Fig. 4.4

(ii) From the same table, the area from − ∞ to 3 is 0·99865, so the area to the right of 3 is 0·00135. But the curve is symmetrical, so the area to the left of −3 is also 0·00135, which is the probability that the variate should be less than −3.

(iii) The area from − ∞ to 2·5 is 0·99379; that from − ∞ to 1·5 is 0·9332. The difference gives us the area from 1·5 to 2·5, i.e. 0·0606, which is the probability that the variate should lie between 1·5 and 2·5.

Question 3. Use the table on p. 188 to find the probability that a normally distributed variate should: (i) exceed 2·5, (ii) lie between 0·5 and 1·0, (iii) be less that 1·5, (iv) lie between −0·5 and 0·5, (v) lie between −1·0 and 1·5.

Mean and standard deviation

4.10. When we were considering a *discrete* variate, we defined the mean and standard deviation by the formulae

$$\mu = \sum Px \ \textbf{(10)} \quad \text{and} \quad \sigma = \sqrt{\{\sum P(x-\mu)^2\}} \ \textbf{(12)}$$

We are now concerned with a continuous variate and so our formulae must be modified. The distribution will be represented, not by a histogram, but by a *probability curve* having the property that the area under it between two values of the variate represents the probability that the variate should lie between these values. If a probability curve has the equation $y = \phi(x)$, the probability that the variate lies between x and $x + \delta x$ is approximately

$$P = \phi(x)\,\delta x$$

and $\phi(x)$ is called a *probability function*.

The formulae $\mu = \sum Px$ and $\sigma^2 = \sum P(x-\mu)^2$ suggest that we should write for a continuous variate

$$\mu \simeq \sum x \cdot \phi(x)\,\delta x \quad \text{and} \quad \sigma^2 \simeq \sum (x-\mu)^2 \cdot \phi(x)\,\delta x$$

Proceeding to the limit we obtain

$$\mu = \int_{-\infty}^{\infty} x\phi(x)\,dx \quad (16) \quad \text{and} \quad \sigma^2 = \int_{-\infty}^{\infty} (x-\mu)^2 \phi(x)\,dx \quad (17)$$

which we shall take to define the mean μ and standard deviation σ of a continuous probability distribution.

$\int_{-\infty}^{\infty} x\phi(x)\,dx$ and $\int_{-\infty}^{\infty} (x-\mu)^2 \phi(x)\,dx$ may be called the *expectation of x* and $(x-\mu)^2$ respectively; more generally $\int_{-\infty}^{\infty} g(x)\phi(x)\,dx$ is the expectation of $g(x)$.

Exercise 4g

1. M. Show that the mean of the normal probability distribution (equation (15)) is zero.

2. M. Find the standard deviation of the normal distribution. (Integrate by parts.)

3. M. A rectangular probability distribution extends from $x = -a$ to $x = a$; find its mean and standard deviation.

4. M.T. Find the probability function of a normal variate with mean μ and standard deviation σ.

Approximations to binomial probabilities

4.11. The normal probability tables can save a great deal of time if we want to find binomial probabilities for large values of n. It should be recalled that we derived the normal distribution from the binomial distribution by the substitution $X = \dfrac{x-\mu}{\sigma}$; this means that to a value of x of the binomial variate there corresponds a value

$$z = \frac{x-\mu}{\sigma}$$

of the normal variate. We shall use z, in this chapter, to denote a *standard normal variate* with unit standard deviation. From Exercise 4g, No. 2, we see that the probability function is

$$\phi(z) = \frac{1}{\sqrt{(2\pi)}} \, e^{-\frac{1}{2}z^2}$$

Example 6. *Estimate from the normal probability table the probability of getting the following with* 100 *spins of a coin*: (*i*) *exactly* 50 *heads*, (*ii*) *more than* 60 *heads.*

The probabilities of obtaining 0, 1, 2, ..., 100 heads are given by the terms of the expansion of $(\frac{1}{2}+\frac{1}{2})^{100}$. By **(11)** $\mu = np = 100 \times \frac{1}{2} = 50$ and by **(14)** $\sigma = \sqrt{(npq)} = \sqrt{(100 \times \frac{1}{2} \times \frac{1}{2})} = 5$.

(i) The area of the binomial histogram corresponding to 50 heads is bounded by $x = 49\frac{1}{2}$ and $x = 50\frac{1}{2}$. The corresponding values of the normal variate are

$$z = \frac{49\frac{1}{2} - 50}{5} \quad \text{and} \quad \frac{50\frac{1}{2} - 50}{5}$$

i.e. $-0\cdot1$ and $0\cdot1$. From the table of p. 188 the area under the normal curve from $-\infty$ to $0\cdot1$ is $0\cdot5398$, so that area from 0 to $0\cdot1$ is $0\cdot0398$. Hence the area from $-0\cdot1$ to $0\cdot1$ is twice this, namely $0\cdot0796$. This is the approximate probability of obtaining 50 heads with 100 spins of a coin. (In Exercise 4c, No. 2, p. 46, we obtained $0\cdot080$ by direct calculation.)

(ii) The area of the binomial histogram corresponding to more than 60 heads is bounded by $x = 60\frac{1}{2}$. The corresponding value of the normal variate is

$$z = \frac{60\frac{1}{2} - 50}{5} = 2\cdot1$$

From Table A the area under the normal curve from $-\infty$ to $2\cdot1$ is $0\cdot9821$. Therefore the probability that more than 60 heads should be obtained is $1 - 0\cdot9821 = 0\cdot0179$.

It is a remarkable result (see Exercise 4f, No. 3, p. 55) that an *asymmetrical* binomial distribution approaches the normal distribution as $n \to \infty$. The approximation needs to be used with rather more caution than in the case of the symmetrical distribution: the greater the divergence of p from $\frac{1}{2}$, the greater will n need to be for satisfactory approximation. In Fig. 4.5 we show the histogram of the binomial distribution given by $(\frac{1}{5}+\frac{4}{5})^{100}$ together with the corresponding normal curve. The agreement is quite good but the normal curve would not give an approximation of very great accuracy.

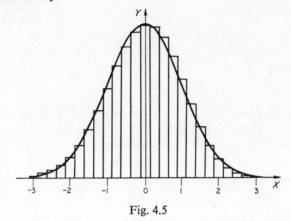

Fig. 4.5

Example 7. *When seeds of a certain type are raised, the probability that a particular plant has wrinkled seeds is $\frac{1}{4}$. When 300 such seeds are raised, what is the probability of obtaining between 70 and 80 plants inclusive, with wrinkled seeds?*

We require an approximation to the terms of the expansion of $(\frac{3}{4}+\frac{1}{4})^{300}$ for integral values of x from 70 to 80 inclusive. The area under the histogram corresponding to these terms lies between $x=69\frac{1}{2}$ and $x=80\frac{1}{2}$. Now by **(11)** $\mu=np=300\times\frac{1}{4}=75$, and by **(14)** $\sigma=\sqrt{(npq)}=\sqrt{(300\times\frac{1}{4}\times\frac{3}{4})}=7\frac{1}{2}$, so the corresponding values of the normal variate are

$$z = \frac{69\frac{1}{2}-75}{7\frac{1}{2}} \quad \text{and} \quad z = \frac{80\frac{1}{2}-75}{7\frac{1}{2}}$$

i.e. $-0.733\ldots$ and $0.733\ldots$. Table A does not give the area under the normal curve from $-\infty$ to $0.733\ldots$ and so we have to interpolate:

The value corresponding to 0.73 is 0.7673

The value corresponding to 0.74 is 0.7704

The difference is 0.0031

but $0.733\ldots$ is $\frac{1}{3}$ of the way from 0.73 to 0.74, so we must add $\frac{1}{3}$ of the difference to the value corresponding to 0.73. Hence the value corresponding to $0.733\ldots$ is

$$0.7673+\tfrac{1}{3}\times0.0031 = 0.7683$$

So the area under the normal curve from $-\infty$ to $0.733\ldots$ is approximately 0.7683. Hence the area from 0 to $0.733\ldots$ is $0.7683-0.5000=0.2683$.

The area from $-0.733\ldots$ to $0.733\ldots$ is twice this, namely 0.5366. Therefore the probability of from 70 to 80 plants with wrinkled seeds is approximately 0.54.

Note: An alternative method of interpolation (well-suited to machines) is to say that we want the value of P which divides the range 0.7673 to 0.7704 in the ratio $1:2$, which is $\frac{2}{3} \times 0.7673 + \frac{1}{3} \times 0.7704 = 0.7683$.

Exercise 4h

1. Taking the probability that a boy is left-handed to be 0.1, find the probability that there are in a school of 900 boys (i) more than 112 left-handed boys, (ii) less than 75 left-handed boys.

2. There are equal numbers of red and black numerals on a roulette wheel. When the wheel is spun 400 times, what is the chance of obtaining more than 210 black numerals?

3. Assuming that the chance of a football match being a draw is $\frac{1}{4}$, what is the probability of there being less than 300 draws in the first 1000 matches of the season?

Normal frequency distributions

4.12. Just as with the binomial distribution, it is sometimes more convenient to work with a theoretical frequency distribution than with a probability distribution when using the normal curve. Such distributions may have means other than zero, and the standard deviation may not be 1. However, in order to use Table A we shall have to work with the standard normal curve

$$y = \frac{1}{\sqrt{(2\pi)}} e^{-\frac{1}{2}z^2} \tag{15}$$

This is illustrated in the next example.

Example 8. 5000 *light bulbs with a mean life of* 120 *days are installed in a new factory; their length of life is normally distributed with standard deviation* 20 *days.* (i) *How many will expire in less than* 90 *days?* (ii) *If it is decided to replace all the bulbs together, what interval should be allowed between replacements if not more than* 10 *per cent should expire before replacement?*

(i) We have $\mu = 120$ days and $\sigma = 20$ days, so the value of the normal probability variate corresponding to 90 days is

$$z = \frac{90 - 120}{20} = -1.5$$

From Table A, the area under the curve from $-\infty$ to $1\cdot5$ is $0\cdot9332$. Hence the area from $1\cdot5$ to $+\infty$ is $1-0\cdot9332=0\cdot0668$ and this, by the symmetry of the curve, is equal to the area from $-\infty$ to $-1\cdot5$. We may therefore expect $5000\times0\cdot0668=334$ bulbs to expire in less than 90 days.

(ii) We need to find the value z of the normal variate such that the area from $-\infty$ to z is $0\cdot1$; we do this by finding the value of the variate z' such that the area from $-\infty$ to z' is $0\cdot9$, then $z=-z'$.

The area from $-\infty$ to $1\cdot28$ is $0\cdot8997$

The area from $-\infty$ to $1\cdot29$ is $0\cdot9015$

$\qquad$ The difference is $0\cdot0018$

The difference between $0\cdot8997$ and $0\cdot9000$ is $0\cdot0003$

Therefore the value of the normal variate corresponding to z' is

$$1\cdot28+\frac{0\cdot0003}{0\cdot0018}\times0\cdot01 = 1\cdot28+0\cdot0017 \simeq 1\cdot282$$

Hence $z=1\cdot282$, so the corresponding number of days d is given by

$$\frac{d-120}{20} = -1\cdot282$$

$$d = 120-20\times1\cdot282 = 94\cdot36$$

So the bulbs would have to be replaced after 94 days.

Exercise 4i

1. Intelligence quotients estimated from certain tests have a mean 100 and standard deviation 15. Find the probability that: (i) such an I.Q. exceeds 130, (ii) such an I.Q. lies between 120 and 130.

If entrance to a grammar school were to be awarded to the 20 per cent of an age group with the highest I.Q.s, what would be the borderline mark?

2. A class estimates the width of a room by counting the number of shoe-lengths across the room. If the width of the room is $23\cdot3$ ft and the measurements are normally distributed about this as mean with standard deviation $0\cdot7$, within what range would you expect (i) half the measurements to lie, (ii) 95 per cent of the measurements to lie?

3. The heights of 2517 men requiring life insurance had mean $69\cdot5$ in. and standard deviation $2\cdot55$ in. (i) Within what limits do the heights of half these men lie? Take the limits symmetrically either side of the mean. (ii) What is the probability that one of these men chosen at random should be more than 6 ft tall? (D. M. Lyon, *Clinical journal*, 71 (1942), 241.)

4. In a newspaper article it stated that the height of 90 per cent of the male population lies between 5 ft $1\frac{3}{4}$ in. and 6 ft $1\frac{1}{2}$ in. Assuming that the distribution of height is normal and that the two limits are placed symmetrically with respect to the mean, what values can be deduced for the mean and standard deviation of the heights?

5. When a long column of figures (each rounded to the same degree of accuracy) is added, the error in the sum introduced by rounding is approximately normally distributed. If 60 numbers are rounded to the nearest unit and then added, the standard deviation of the error may be taken to be 2·24; within what limits (symmetrically placed) would (i) half, (ii) 95 per cent of the errors lie?

Probability paper*

4.13. Distributions such as those in Exercise 4i cannot be exactly normal but approximate to it satisfactorily. The simplest way to test whether a distribution is approximately normal is to use arithmetical probability paper. This has a uniform scale one way (see Fig. 4.7); the other scale is obtained from the normal distribution by marking off on the x-axis the percentage of the distribution to the left of that point (see Fig. 4.6). Pads of such paper may be obtained from W. Heffer & Sons Ltd, Sidney Street, Cambridge.

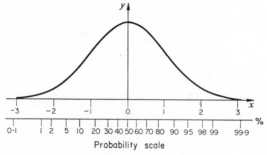

Fig. 4.6

Suppose, now, that a frequency distribution is normally distributed, we can in a similar fashion find the percentage of the distribution to the left of any value of the variate (this is called the *cumulative percentage*), then the scale of percentages obtained should be the same as the probability scale, except for a scale factor depending on the standard deviation of the distribution (e.g. if the standard deviation is 2, the percentage points will be twice the distance apart compared with the probability scale). Hence, if we plot the cumulative percentage against the probability scale, we should obtain a straight line if the distribution is normal.

Consider, for example, the distribution of Exercise 2e, No. 9, heights of 2517 men requiring life insurance.

* The remainder of the chapter may be omitted.

| Height (in.) | | Frequency | Cumulative frequency | Cumulative percentage |
mid-value	end-value			
60·5		0		
	61		0	0
61·5		3		
	62		3	0·1
62·5		10		
	63		13	0·5
63·5		26		
	64		39	1·5
64·5		53		
	65		92	3·6
65·5		106		
	66		198	7·8
66·5		195		
	67		393	15·6
67·5		301		
	68		694	27·6
68·5		381		
	69		1075	42·7
69·5		369		
	70		1444	57·4
70·5		383		
	71		1827	72·6
71·5		269		
	72		2096	83·3
72·5		186		
	73		2282	90·7
73·5		137		
	74		2419	96·1
74·5		54		
	75		2473	98·3
75·5		26		
	76		2499	99·3
76·5		15		
	77		2514	99·9
77·5		2		
	78		2516	99·96
78·5		1		
	79		2517	100

The *cumulative frequency*, which is the sum of the frequencies higher in the table, may be regarded as the *integral*, from $-\infty$ to x, of whatever function gives the frequency. Note that the cumulative frequency and the cumulative percentage correspond to the *end-values* of the variate, while the frequencies correspond to the mid-values. In Fig. 4.7 the cumulative

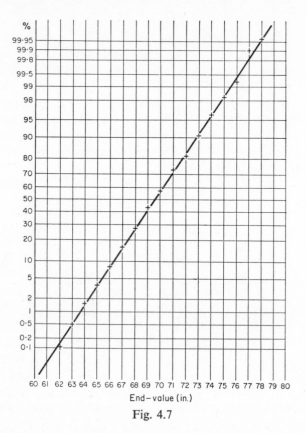

Fig. 4.7

percentages have been marked off against the corresponding end-values of the variate shown on the horizontal axis and against the percentages shown on the vertical axis. A straight line has been drawn on the graph and it will be seen that all the points lie on or near it, showing that the distribution is approximately normal.

We can also use the graph to fit a normal distribution, although the values we obtain will not be very accurate. Where the line meets the ordinates through the end-values, we read off the cumulative percentages and tabulate them below.

End-value	60	61	62	63	64	65	66	67	68	69	70
Cum. %		0·03	0·14	0·48	1·3	3·4	7·8	16	27	41	57
Cum. frequency		1	4	12	33	86	196	403	680	1032	1435
Frequency	1	3	8	21	53	110	207	277	352	403	

70	71	72	73	74	75	76	77	78	79	80
57	71	83	91	96	98·4	99·4	99·84	99·96	99·99	
1435	1787	2089	2290	2416	2477	2502	2513	2516	2517	
	352	302	201	126	61	25	11	3	1	

The cumulative frequencies are obtained from the cumulative percentages by multiplying by a factor of $\frac{2517}{100}$, 2517 being the number in the original distribution. The frequencies are the differences between successive cumulative frequencies. For comparison with the original distribution, the two sets of frequencies are shown together below.

Mid-value	60·5	61·5	62·5	63·5	64·5	65·5	66·5	67·5	68·5	69·5
Observed frequency	0	3	10	26	53	106	195	301	381	369
Normal frequency	1	3	8	21	53	110	207	277	352	403

70·5	71·5	72·5	73·5	74·5	75·5	76·5	77·5	78·5	79·5
383	269	186	137	54	26	15	2	1	
352	302	201	126	61	25	11	3	1	

Since an error of 1 in the last place of the cumulative percentage will make a considerable difference to some of the frequencies, this method is a very rough one. However, the agreement between these sets of frequencies is clearly quite good, especially when it is remembered that an inaccuracy of $\frac{1}{2}$ per cent (the central cumulative percentages being estimated to the nearest 1 per cent) would lead to an error of $12\frac{1}{2}$ in the cumulative frequency. A discussion of goodness of fit is delayed until Chapter 8.

If probability paper is not available, or greater accuracy is required, the normal probabilities may be calculated. The method is rather laborious but is illustrated in the next section.

Fitting a normal distribution

4.14. The process of fitting a normal distribution to a frequency or probability distribution is rather laborious, as we warned you in the last section. We have therefore taken a simple example which will illustrate the method and be easier to follow than the fitting of an observed frequency distribution.

Example 9. *Fit a normal distribution to the binomial distribution* $(\frac{1}{2}+\frac{1}{2})^{16}$.

From **(11)** and **(14)** we have $\mu=np=8$, $\sigma=\sqrt{(npq)}=\sqrt{(16\times\frac{1}{2}\times\frac{1}{2})}=2$. Since the distribution is symmetrical it is not necessary to consider all values of the variate.

Variate mid-value	end-value x	$x-\mu$	$z=\dfrac{x-\mu}{\sigma}$	P	ΔP	Binomial probability
7						
	$7\frac{1}{2}$	$-\frac{1}{2}$	$-0\cdot25$	$0\cdot4013$		
8					$0\cdot1974$	$0\cdot1964$
	$8\frac{1}{2}$	$\frac{1}{2}$	$0\cdot25$	$0\cdot5987$		
9					$0\cdot1747$	$0\cdot1746$
	$9\frac{1}{2}$	$1\frac{1}{2}$	$0\cdot75$	$0\cdot7734$		
10					$0\cdot1210$	$0\cdot1222$
	$10\frac{1}{2}$	$2\frac{1}{2}$	$1\cdot25$	$0\cdot8944$		
11					$0\cdot0655$	$0\cdot0667$
	$11\frac{1}{2}$	$3\frac{1}{2}$	$1\cdot75$	$0\cdot9599$		
12					$0\cdot0279$	$0\cdot0278$
	$12\frac{1}{2}$	$4\frac{1}{2}$	$2\cdot25$	$0\cdot9878$		
13					$0\cdot00922$	$0\cdot0085$
	$13\frac{1}{2}$	$5\frac{1}{2}$	$2\cdot75$	$0\cdot99702$		
14					$0\cdot00240$	$0\cdot0018$
	$14\frac{1}{2}$	$6\frac{1}{2}$	$3\cdot25$	$0\cdot99942$		
15					$0\cdot00049$	$0\cdot0002$
	$15\frac{1}{2}$	$7\frac{1}{2}$	$3\cdot75$	$0\cdot99991$		
16					$0\cdot00009$	$0\cdot0000$
	$16\frac{1}{2}$	$8\frac{1}{2}$	$4\cdot25$	$1\cdot00000$		

We work with the end-values so that we can find the probability P that a normal variate lies between the corresponding limits given by $(x-\mu)/\sigma$. Values of P have been found from the normal probability table, Table A. ΔP is the difference between successive values of P and therefore gives the normal probabilities corresponding to 8, 9, ..., 16 successes. For convenience of comparison the binomial probabilities are given alongside. If a theoretical frequency distribution is preferred, the probabilities may be multiplied by n the desired total frequency.

Exercise 4j

If no probability paper is available, tracing paper can be clipped to Fig. 4.7 and the ruling on that used, however probability paper should give better results as more lines are ruled on it.

1. L. Use probability paper to fit a normal distribution to the data of Exercise 2d, No. 3. Comment on the result.

2. L. Use probability paper to fit a normal distribution to the data of Exercise 2e, No. 8. The data may be grouped to smooth out some of the irregularities; in the answers end-values of 32·35, 32·75, etc. have been taken.

3. Sketch the graph that would be obtained from plotting the cumulative percentages of a rectangular distribution on probability paper. Verify your conclusions by plotting points.

4. The distribution of lengths of 995 telephone calls is given below. The mean and standard deviation are 477·3 and 148·4 sec respectively. Complete the calculations to find the frequencies of the normal distribution fitting the data.

Observed frequency	End-value x	$x-m$	$z=\dfrac{x-m}{s}$	P	$995P$	Normal frequency
	0					
1						5·4
	99·5	−377·8	−2·546	0·0054	5·4	
28						25·0
	199·5	−277·8	−1·872	0·0306	30·4	
88						84·5
	299·5	−177·8	−1·198	0·1155	114·9	
180						183·6
	399·5	−77·8	−0·5243	0·3000		
247						
	499·5	22·2				
260						
	599·5	122·2				
133						
	699·5	222·2				
42						
	799·5	322·2				
11						
	899·5	422·2	2·845	0·997 78	992·8	
5						2·0
	999·5	522·2	3·519	0·999 78	994·8	
						0·2

(J. F. Kenney, *Mathematics of statistics.*)

5. 1000 shots were fired at a line drawn on a target. Belts of equal breadth were drawn on the target, all being parallel to the line. The observed frequency of shots hitting each belt is given below.

Belt no.	1	2	3	4	5	6	7	8	9	10	11	Total
Frequency	1	4	10	89	190	212	204	193	79	16	2	1000

Fit a normal distribution to this data. (K. Pearson, *Phil. Mag.* 50 (1900), 173, quoting Prof. Merriman.)

6. M.T. An informal method of showing that

$$\int_{-\infty}^{\infty} e^{-\frac{1}{2}x^2} dx = \sqrt{(2\pi)}$$

First observe that

$$\int_{-\infty}^{\infty} e^{-\frac{1}{2}x^2} dx \int_{-\infty}^{\infty} e^{-\frac{1}{2}y^2} dy = \int_{-\infty}^{\infty} \int_{-\infty}^{\infty} e^{-\frac{1}{2}(x^2+y^2)} dx\,dy$$

Evaluate by changing to polar coordinates. More formally, consider the integral

$$\int_{0}^{a} \int_{0}^{a} e^{-\frac{1}{2}(x^2+y^2)} dx\,dy$$

7. M. Calculation of normal probabilities.

(i)

$$\frac{1}{\sqrt{(2\pi)}} \int_{0}^{1} e^{-\frac{1}{2}x^2} dx$$

Find the first six terms of the expansion of $e^{-\frac{1}{2}x^2}$ in ascending powers of x; integrate term by term between the limits 0 and 1; divide by $\sqrt{(2\pi)} = 2\cdot5066$.

(*Note*: Although this method works for this integral, we have not justified the process; the series converges slowly for larger values of x and the method below is more appropriate.)

(ii)

$$\frac{1}{\sqrt{(2\pi)}} \int_{3}^{\infty} e^{-\frac{1}{2}x^2} dx$$

If

$$I_n = \int_{x}^{\infty} \frac{e^{-\frac{1}{2}x^2}}{x^n} dx$$

show that

$$I_n = \frac{e^{-\frac{1}{2}x^2}}{x^{n+1}} - (n+1) I_{n+2}$$

Deduce that

$$I_0 = e^{-\frac{1}{2}x^2} \left(\frac{1}{x} - \frac{1}{x^3} + \frac{3}{x^5} - \frac{3.5}{x^7} + \frac{3.5.7}{x^9} \right) - 3.5.7.9\, I_9$$

Hence find the required integral. The error is

$$\frac{3.5.7.9}{\sqrt{(2\pi)}} I_9$$

CHAPTER 5

Tests of significance I

Sampling

5.1. In 1936, before the United States Presidential election when Franklin D. Roosevelt was elected, a magazine conducted a survey of over a million people and came to the conclusion that Alfred M. Landon would easily be elected; in fact Roosevelt's victory was a decisive one. This, however, is not the whole story—two sociologists, Gallup and Roper conducted another survey with only 5000 people and correctly predicted Roosevelt's win. How can this have come about? Was it just luck that Gallup and Roper were successful?

The answer to the last question is, 'No !' The two sociologists planned their sample carefully so that it would be representative of the electors, including the correct proportion of men and women, whites and negroes, rich and poor etc. But the magazine obtained the names of the people in its survey from the pages of telephone directories and so introduced a bias into its sample because people who have telephones in their homes tend to be richer than average—and Roosevelt's election programme appealed particularly to those who were less well off.

The way round this difficulty of introducing bias into a sample is to take what is known as a *random sample*, that is, a sample in which every individual has an equal chance of being selected. Clearly in the illustration above, people without telephones had no chance of being selected and so the sample was not random. In practice, surveys often use 'stratified' random samples in which certain proportions of people in different age groups, income groups etc., are determined from a knowledge of the population concerned. Then within these groups people are selected at random.

In the last paragraph, the word 'population' was introduced in very much its usual conversational sense. A *population* in statistics may be a set of people, such as the adult male population of Great Britain, or we may refer to a set of measurements, for instance the heights of these people. Care should be taken in defining the populations under consideration, for instance, 'English girls' would not be clear because the age limits are not defined—what is the upper age for a girl? Indeed, just as for any other set, it must be possible to determine whether any individual belongs to the set or not.

An obvious way of trying to obtain a random sample is to take every tenth, twentieth (or any other convenient number) individual. This however can on occasions introduce bias; for instance, a machine might be producing faulty articles periodically and, if the two intervals were the same, the fault might not be noticed. So it is common practice to use tables of random numbers to determine which individuals are to be examined. A number is assigned to every individual in the population, we decide how many individuals we want in our sample, say n, and choose the first n individuals whose numbers appear when we look down the columns in the table. The number of individuals in a sample we shall call its *size*.

Tables of random numbers which have been field-tested are readily available, but you can build up your own table by spinning coins. Suppose we want random numbers between 1 and 100, inclusive, we should need 8 coins. Spinning them in order and counting 1 for a head and 0 for a tail, we obtain binary numbers, e.g. HTTHHHT in this order gives us the binary number 1001110 or 78 in the scale of 10. Numbers greater than 100 are rejected. ERNIE was built simply to produce random numbers for the awarding of prizes to holders of premium bonds.

There is a particular type of random sample which is of theoretical importance: this is the *simple* sample. The meaning of this term can conveniently be illustrated by drawing cards from a pack. We could number 100 cards with the integers from 1 to 100 and draw a random sample by shuffling the pack well and taking as many cards as we needed without looking at the numbers. But if we wanted a simple sample, we should have to return each card to the pack and reshuffle before the next card was chosen. By this means we ensure that the probability of any card being chosen is exactly the same on each occasion.

Sampling distributions

5.2. Suppose that an opinion poll is being conducted before a by-election in a constituency where the result is expected to be a close one and that the Labour candidate is supported by 48 per cent of those asked, the Conservative candidate by 47 per cent of those asked and 5 per cent have not decided between the two candidates. It is clearly a matter of importance to the election agents to know whether these proportions are accurate estimates of the situation; if either of the percentages may be out by as much as 3 per cent, the result of the election could easily go either way.

So what we turn to next is a discussion of the variation that can be expected between different samples from the same population.*

Try the following experiment, or invent one like it for yourself to try. (Class teachers may like to use a sampling bottle.) Select ten numbers at random from 0, 1, 2, ..., 98, 99. Find the mean of the ten numbers selected, and repeat this until you have a sizeable distribution of means. The numbers may be selected in various ways: from the last two digits of telephone numbers in a directory,† from tables of random numbers, or by numbering cards from 0 to 99. (If cards are used, after each card is drawn, record the number, replace the card and shuffle the pack—it is rather a slow method but brings out the idea of a random sample.) The author found 50 means with random number tables and obtained the distribution shown in Fig. 5.1.

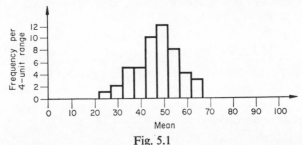

Fig. 5.1

This histogram illustrates the general idea that, if we take samples from a population, the mean of the sample cannot be expected to be exactly equal to the mean of the population. If we take a number of samples, as I did above, the mean itself will have a frequency distribution; if we considered all the possible samples, it would be possible to find the probability distribution for the mean. Similarly any other *statistic* such as standard deviation, proportion, and others to be found later in the book, will have a probability distribution which is governed by (1) the population from which the sample is drawn and (2) the size of the sample. Such probability distributions are called *sampling distributions* and in the next section we discuss one which can easily be found theoretically.

Exercise 5a

1. L. As a measure of the variation of the mean, find the standard deviation of the distribution in the experiment above. Find the ratio of this to

---

* Added point is given to this paragraph by the fact that it was written a few hours *before* the unexpected defeat of the Labour Foreign Secretary, Mr Patrick Gordon Walker, at Leyton in January 1965.

† These may not be completely random, but will do for this experiment.

the standard deviation of the population. (*Hint*: For the latter, use formulae
(4a) and **(9)**, and $\sum_1^n r^2 = \frac{1}{6}n(n+1)(2n+1)$.)

2. (Suitable for cooperative work.) In a population, values of the variate
are found in proportions given by the following table:

Variate x	1	2	3	4	5	6	Total
Frequency f	2	5	6	4	2	1	20

Take 20 beans and use a felt pen to mark (both sides) with values of the
variate given by the table. (Better still, get a friend to mark a set for you
with a distribution unknown to you.) Use a small tin to mix them up in,
and draw samples of size n (see below), replacing and mixing up after
each bean is drawn. Tabulate the means of 50 or more such samples,
displaying the results on a histogram. Find the ratio of the standard
deviation of the distribution of means to that of the population.

Note: it is suggested that individual readers should take $n = 5$. If a class
is working this question, samples of different sizes may be taken; in this
case, see if you can discover an experimental law connecting the standard
deviation of the distribution of means of samples of size n and that of the
population.

3. Select ten numbers at random as suggested in §5.2. This time record the
proportion of odd numbers in each sample. Display your results in a histogram and find the standard deviation of the distribution of proportions.

4. Discuss how you could obtain from the county in which you live
random samples of: (i) 13-year-old boys, (ii) women between 25 and 30.

5. Discuss how you would estimate the following:

(i) the number of seeds in a pound of grass seed,

(ii) the number of dandelion plants on a games field,

(iii) the number of cars entering and leaving a town by two specified
roads in a given week,

(iv) the number of families with refrigerators in a local town.

6. Find examples, such as that provided by a greengrocer who displays his
best apples in the window, of samples which are deliberately biased.

Sampling distribution of a proportion

5.3. One of the simplest and most commonly used statistics is the *proportion*. If it is possible to classify individuals into two mutually exclusive

sets, such as males and females, we may be interested in the proportions of individuals in the two sets. (Sometimes the figures are given in percentages but these can easily be converted into proportions by dividing by 100.) Or consider another example: the tax allowance given to the parents of a child runs from the beginning of the year in which he (or she) is born, the tax year beginning in April; it is held that some parents try to obtain the allowance for the whole year and yet keep expenditure on the baby down to a minimum by timing his arrival in March—do the following figures give evidence of such a tendency? In March 1960 there were 66 400 legitimate live births in England and Wales, while in the whole year there were 740 000 such births, both being given to three significant figures, the data being calculated from figures given in The Registrar General's *Statistical review of England and Wales*, 1961. Now March has 31 days and 1960 had 366, being a leap year, so if the births were distributed uniformly throughout the year we should expect

$$\frac{31}{366} \times 740\,000 = 62\,700$$

births during March. Clearly the difference between the observed and expected values $66\,400 - 62\,700 = 3700$ is considerable, but might it not have arisen by chance? What we need is some indication of the sort of variation which might be expected. The way we are going to tackle it is through the corresponding proportions.

The proportion of births expected during March 1960 was

$$\frac{31}{366} = 0.0847$$

while the proportion observed was

$$\frac{66\,400}{740\,000} = 0.0897$$

The difference between the observed and expected proportions is $0.0897 - 0.0847 = 0.0050$. But before we can go further we shall have to find the standard deviation of the sampling distribution of a proportion.

For the general case, consider samples of size n where the probability of a success in any trial is p. (We return to the terminology introduced in §4.4, p. 44.) The sampling distribution of the proportion of successes is then given by the probabilities of obtaining proportions of 0, $1/n$, ..., r/n, ..., 1 success in a sample; this we shall obtain from the binomial distribution (p. 45):

No. of successes x	0	1	...	r		... n
Probability P	q^n	$nq^{n-1}p$	...	$\dfrac{n!}{(n-r)!\,r!}q^{n-r}p^r$		... p^n

But the proportions of successes are respectively

$$0 \quad \frac{1}{n} \quad ... \quad \frac{r}{n} \quad ... \quad 1$$

so that the probabilities of these proportions of successes in n trials are:

Proportion of successes x	0	$\dfrac{1}{n}$	...	$\dfrac{r}{n}$		... 1
Probability P	q^n	$nq^{n-1}p$	...	$\dfrac{n!}{(n-r)!\,r!}q^{n-r}p^r$		... p^n

The mean of the number of successes $\mu = \sum Px = np$ **(11)**, hence the mean of the proportions

$$\sum P\frac{x}{n} = \frac{1}{n}\sum Px = p$$

The standard deviation of the number of successes σ is given by

$$\sigma^2 = \sum P(x-\mu)^2 = \sum P(x-np)^2 = npq \qquad \text{(by (14))}$$

hence the standard deviation of the proportions

$$\sum P\left(\frac{x}{n}-p\right)^2 = \frac{1}{n^2}\sum P(x-np)^2 = \frac{npq}{n^2} = \frac{pq}{n}$$

The standard deviation of a sampling distribution is called the *standard error* of the statistic involved, so we say the

$$\textbf{standard error of a proportion } \sigma_p = \sqrt{\frac{pq}{n}} \qquad \textbf{(18)}$$

The term 'standard error' reflects the interest in errors of observation early in the development of the theory of probability. The deviation of a statistic (e.g., a proportion, mean or standard deviation) from the true value in the population may be thought of as an 'error' of estimation; then the standard error provides a standard against which the 'error' may be compared. It is also helpful to be able to distinguish easily between the standard *deviation* of the sample and the standard *error* of a sampling distribution.

Now we can return to the problem of the March babies; here the size of the sample $n = 740000$. On the assumption of a uniform distribution of births throughout the year (an example of the rectangular distribution, incidentally), the probability of a child being born in March $p = \frac{31}{366} = 0.0847$ and this, as we have seen above, is also the mean of the distribution of proportions. Now the standard deviation, or standard error, of the distribution

$$\sigma_p = \sqrt{\frac{pq}{n}} = \sqrt{\frac{0.0847 \times 0.9153}{740000}} = \sqrt{0.000001048} = 0.00102$$

But the observed deviation from 0.0847 we have already found to be 0.0050, hence the *critical ratio*

$$\frac{\text{deviation}}{\text{standard error}} = \frac{0.0050}{0.00102} = 4.9$$

Now we have previously found very few observed values of a variate which are at a distance of more than 3σ from the mean so we conclude that it is very unlikely that the observed proportion of legitimate live births in March 1960 should have arisen by chance. We cannot, however, infer that the *cause* of this is the tax allowance: the discussion of this must be left to those with special knowledge of subjects such as psychology, sociology and physiology.

Note. The factor of 3 times the standard deviation is an arbitrary one but we can estimate the probability that the critical ratio should exceed this amount. We have seen that the binomial distribution approaches the normal distribution as the size of sample tends to infinity, and that the distribution of proportions is simply the binomial distribution with a different scale on the x-axis. Now, when we divide the deviation from the mean by the standard deviation, the scale factor cancels out and thereby allows us to calculate probabilities from the normal distribution, the value of n here being large. From the normal probability table (Table A, p. 188) the probability of a normal variate being at a distance of more than 3σ from the mean is 0.0027, which is less than three thousandths.

Example 1. *In a certain survey the births of 8800 boys and 8200 girls were recorded. Are these figures consistent with the hypothesis that an unborn baby is equally likely to be a boy or a girl?* (N. R. Butler and D. G. Bonham, *Perinatal mortality*, figures rounded.)

The number of births recorded $n = 8800 + 8200 = 17000$.

The proportion of male births $= \dfrac{8000}{17000} = 0.5176$.

On the hypothesis that the probability of a male birth is $\frac{1}{2}$, the mean value of the sampling distribution of the proportion is $\frac{1}{2}$. The standard deviation, or standard error, of the proportion

$$\sqrt{\frac{pq}{n}} = \sqrt{\frac{\frac{1}{2} \times \frac{1}{2}}{17000}} = \sqrt{0.00001471} = 0.00384$$

The observed deviation from 0.5 is 0.0176, so the critical ratio

$$\frac{\text{deviation}}{\text{standard error}} = \frac{0.0176}{0.00384} = 4.59$$

This ratio is so much greater than 3 that we conclude that the hypothesis is very unlikely to be correct. (It is just possible that, on these data, the hypothesis is correct, but if there were no supporting evidence we should reject the hypothesis. In fact it is consistently found, in this country, that more boys are born than girls.)

Exercise 5b

1. The time of birth was noted for 16994 babies:

36.1 per cent were born between midnight and 8 a.m.,

30.3 per cent were born between 8 a.m. and 4 p.m.

Do these percentages differ significantly from $33\frac{1}{3}$ per cent? (Butler and Bonham, *op. cit.*)

2. In crosses of a certain pea, 5321 had yellow seeds and 1804 had green seeds. Do these numbers suggest a significant departure from the expected Mendelian ratio $3:1$? (W. Bateson, E. R. Saunders, and R. C. Punnett, *Second report of the Evolution Committee of the Royal Society* (1905), 72.)

3. In a Mendelian experiment the length of stem was noted for 1064 pea plants; 787 were tall and 277 were dwarf. Are these numbers consistent with the expected proportions of $3:1$? (*Encyclopaedia Britannica* (1953) 15, 241.)

Null hypothesis

5.4. It is worth while having a closer look at the method of Example 1 because this kind of argument will be used extensively in the different tests of significance that follow in this book. The first step was to set up a hypothesis that an unborn baby is equally likely to be a boy or a girl.

This is an example of a *null hypothesis*, that is to say, a hypothesis which is not binding. This should be stated explicitly as there are occasions when more than one null hypothesis (see below Example 2) might be set up.

The next stage was to work out the consequences of this hypothesis and we found it was highly improbable that the data should have been obtained by simple sampling from a population such as that described by the hypothesis, i.e. where an unborn baby had an equal chance of being a boy or a girl; consequently we rejected the hypothesis. We can never prove by taking a sample that any statement about a population is false: we should have to examine the whole population (or nearly so, depending on the statement involved) to do this—what we can do is to give an objective assessment of the probabilities involved. This is done in the next example.

Example 2. *In a count of letters from a page of a book there were found 121 consonants and 91 vowels. Is this consistent with the hypothesis that there are equal numbers of consonants and vowels used in the book?*

There are two points worth noting: (1) the count may not be a random sample—there is nothing said about this, (2) the count was made only from one page, so that we shall not be sure whether the proportion of vowels varies from one part of the book to another. On the other hand it may be held that the proportion of vowels is not likely to vary a great deal and so we shall tentatively examine the data.

We wish to test the hypothesis that the probability of a letter chosen at random being a vowel is $\frac{1}{2}$. From **(18)**, taking $p=q=\frac{1}{2}$ and $n=121+91$ $=212$, the standard error of the proportion

$$\sigma_p = \sqrt{\frac{pq}{n}} = \sqrt{\frac{\frac{1}{2} \times \frac{1}{2}}{212}} = \sqrt{\frac{1}{848}} = \sqrt{0.001\,179} = 0.034\,34$$

The observed proportion of vowels $= \dfrac{91}{212} = 0.4292$

The expected proportion $p=0.5000$.

Hence the deviation from the expected proportion $= 0.4292 - 0.5000$
$$= -0.0718$$

$$\therefore \frac{\text{deviation}}{\text{standard error}} = -\frac{0.0718}{0.034\,34} = -2.091$$

Since the number in the sample is large we may use the normal probability table, Table A, to find the probability that the deviation should numerically exceed 0·0718. From the table we find that the probability the normal variate should exceed 2·091 is $1 - 0.9817 = 0.0183$; hence the probability that the normal variate should numerically exceed 2·091 is 2×0.0183 $=0.0366$. So we find that the probability of a deviation numerically greater than 0·0718 occurring by chance is 0·0366, or about 1 chance in 27.

As often happens, the result is rather inconclusive; if a decision about cost came into the matter, it would be desirable to get further evidence; if a bet were being made, most people would, I suspect, bet that the numbers of consonants and vowels in the book differ considerably; if your prestige as a statistician were being considered as a result of your decision, you would, in the long run, only be wrong one time in 27 with such a probability if you rejected the hypothesis—and anyway you would point out the flaws in the data to cover yourself! Still, the example serves to show the sort of circumstances that have given rise to what are known as 'levels of significance'.

Another point arising from Example 2 is that we could equally well have chosen other hypotheses to test. For instance, is the result of the count consistent with the hypothesis that consonants and vowels are in the ratio 2:1? In this case, the probability that a letter chosen at random is a vowel is taken to be $p = \frac{1}{3}$; hence $q = \frac{2}{3}$, so from **(18)** the standard error of the proportion

$$\sigma_p = \sqrt{\frac{pq}{n}} = \sqrt{\frac{\frac{1}{3} \times \frac{2}{3}}{212}} = \sqrt{\frac{1}{954}} = \sqrt{0.001\,048} = 0.032\,38$$

The deviation from the expected proportion $= 0.4292 - 0.3333 = 0.0959$

$$\frac{\text{deviation}}{\text{standard error}} = \frac{0.095\,9}{0.032\,38} = 2.96$$

This time we find from Table A that the probability the normal variate should numerically exceed 2·96 is 0·0031, or approximately a chance of 3 in a thousand, which is small enough for us to reject the hypothesis with some confidence.

Levels of significance

5.5. If we say that a certain result is significant at the 5 per cent level, we mean that the probability of such a result having arisen through the fluctuations of random sampling is less than 5 per cent; similarly other levels of significance are used, especially 1 per cent and 0·1 per cent, also sometimes 2 per cent and $2\frac{1}{2}$ per cent. So we would say that the result of Example 2 was significant at the 5 per cent level. Clearly much greater reliance would be placed on a result which was significant at the 1 per cent level or the 0·1 per cent level but sometimes it is difficult to collect very much data, or other factors affect the experiment, in which case a result significant at the 5 per cent level might be of considerable interest. These levels of significance are completely arbitrary: they serve as convenient reference points, the magnitude is easily grasped on reading, and they save the evaluation of more precise probabilities. It should always be remembered that the size of the ratio (deviation):(standard error) *may* be due to random sampling but this will only happen, for instance at the 1 per cent level, less than once in a hundred such results in the long run. By examining work in any field of application of statistics it is possible to see the reliance placed on the different levels of significance by the workers in that field. Here it is worth adding that the statistician never has the last word in a statistical investigation—in any field such as medicine, economics, psychology, etc., it is up to the expert in the field to interpret the results in the light of his special knowledge.

It is useful to know the values of the normal variate corresponding to different levels of significance.

5 % of the distribution lies outside the range $-1\cdot9600$ to $+1\cdot9600$

2 % of the distribution lies outside the range $-2\cdot3263$ to $+2\cdot3263$

1 % of the distribution lies outside the range $-2\cdot5758$ to $+2\cdot5758$

0·1 % of the distribution lies outside the range $-3\cdot2905$ to $+3\cdot2905$

Question 1. Check these figures with Table A, p. 188.

These levels of significance are for what is known as a 'two-tailed' test because both tails of the normal probability distribution are taken into consideration. In Example 2, the hypothesis that the numbers of vowels and consonants were equal would have been contradicted by there being either too many or too few vowels. This is the usual situation that we shall meet but a one-tailed test might arise as follows. Suppose that we are interested in whether a new method of treating people for an illness is better than an established one. Now an established method of treatment is usually retained until it is shown that a new treatment is better, so it would be appropriate to set up the null hypothesis that the new test is no better than the established one. This hypothesis would only be contradicted if there were a *better* recovery rate under the new treatment than under the old; only one tail of the normal distribution corresponds to this situation and so the test is described as 'one-tailed'. From this paragraph it may be seen that the probability we obtain from our analysis will depend on the null hypothesis we make at the beginning of it; hence the importance of stating the hypothesis. Most of the tests in the remainder of this book will be two-tailed and your attention will be called to circumstances for which a one-tailed test is appropriate.

Exercise 5c

1. A simple extra-sensory experiment can be carried out as follows, two people A and B taking part. A pack of playing cards is shuffled and A turns them over one at a time, thinking hard about the colour of the card; B, who cannot see the cards or A, has to record whether he thinks the card is red or black. At least one observer is needed to say when the next card is to be turned—and to stop cheating. You may like to try this experiment for yourself. If in such an experiment B was right for 33 out of 52 cards, would you say there was evidence of telepathy?

2. The fourth decimal figure was examined for 4-figure Naperian logarithms at intervals of 0·1 from 1·0 to 9·9; 54 were found to be odd. To what extent may we conclude that these digits are not random?

3. It is suggested that, in the long run, Oxford and Cambridge have equal chances of winning the boat race. Is this borne out by the record up to 1965 when Oxford had won 49 times and Cambridge 61 times (1 dead-heat excluded)?

4. In a Mendelian experiment by W. Bateson, E. R. Saunders, and R. C. Punnett, (*Third report to the Evolution Committee of the Royal Society*) 1528 sweet pea plants had purple flowers and long pollen out of a total of 2132 plants. The expected proportion was 9/16—can the observed proportion be accounted for by fluctuations of random sampling? (C. D. Darlington, and K. Mather, *The elements of genetics*.)

5. Suppose that a friend has just started reading this book and that you wish to predict limits within which the number of heads will lie when he has performed 100 spins of a coin. If the limits are symmetrically placed either side of 50, and you wish to have a 95 per cent chance of being right, what would you predict? (*Hint:* (deviation):(standard error) $= \pm 1\cdot9600$.) What would your prediction be if you were more cautious and wished to have a 99 per cent chance of being right?

6. During a survey, 2000 people have been interviewed and 40 per cent are in favour of a certain washing powder. If you were in charge of the survey and were reporting on it, between what limits would you say that the actual proportion lies (i) if you wished to have a 95 per cent chance of being correct, (ii) if you wished to have a 99 per cent chance of being correct?

(*Note:* Really we need the probability that a person chosen at random is in favour of the washing powder; as we do not know this we can make an estimate by working with $p = 0\cdot4$.)

7. An opinion poll is required to be correct within x per cent. How many people should be interviewed if the organiser wishes to have a 95 per cent chance of achieving this accuracy? (*Hint:* For what value of p is pq greatest?)

8. Spin a particular drawing pin 100 times and observe the number of times it falls with the pin upright. Assuming that you want to have a 95 per cent chance of being correct, find limits for the probability of it falling this way in any one trial (i) taking p to be equal to the observed proportion of successes, (ii) taking the value of p which maximises the standard error.

Standard error of a mean

5.6. In §5.2, p. 70, we suggested that you should carry out a simple experiment to obtain a distribution of means of samples drawn from the numbers $0, 1, 2, \ldots, 99$. The object then was to draw your attention to the fact that the mean of a sample cannot be expected to be equal to the mean of the population from which it is drawn. We now turn to the problem of finding how much variation is to be expected in the mean of a sample. If we consider all the samples of size n that can be drawn from a given population their means will have a distribution which will have a certain standard deviation (or standard error). What, then, is the standard error of this distribution of means? The theorem which gives us the answer to this question will first be stated and then proved for a very simple case before giving a general proof.

Theorem. If simple samples of size n are taken from a population with standard deviation σ, the standard deviation (standard error) of the mean of such samples is

$$\sigma_m = \frac{\sigma}{\sqrt{n}} \qquad (19)$$

(Note that we shall use *Greek* letters for the mean and standard deviation of a *population*.)

A very simple example will help to bring out the method used for the general proof.* Consider a population of 4 values of a variate x namely a, b, c, d. Let the mean of the population be μ so that $\mu = \frac{1}{4}(a+b+c+d)$. We shall take into account the order in which the samples are chosen so that there are 64 distinct samples containing 3 values of x:

---

* The less mathematical reader may like to skip to the end of the general proof on first reading.

$a, a, a,$	$a, b, a,$	$a, c, a,$	$a, d, a,$	$b, a, a,$	$b, b, a,$	$b, c, a,$	$b, d, a,$
$a, a, b,$	$a, b, b,$	$a, c, b,$	$a, d, b,$	$b, a, b,$	$b, b, b,$	$b, c, b,$	$b, d, b,$
$a, a, c,$	$a, b, c,$	$a, c, c,$	$a, d, c,$	$b, a, c,$	$b, b, c,$	$b, c, c,$	$b, d, c,$
$a, a, d,$	$a, b, d,$	$a, c, d,$	$a, d, d,$	$b, a, d,$	$b, b, d,$	$b, c, d,$	$b, d, d,$
$c, a, a,$	$c, b, a,$	$c, c, a,$	$c, d, a,$	$d, a, a,$	$d, b, a,$	$d, c, a,$	$d, d, a,$
$c, a, b,$	$c, b, b,$	$c, c, b,$	$c, d, b,$	$d, a, b,$	$d, b, b,$	$d, c, b,$	$d, d, b,$
$c, a, c,$	$c, b, c,$	$c, c, c,$	$c, d, c,$	$d, a, c,$	$d, b, c,$	$d, c, c,$	$d, d, c,$
$c, a, d,$	$c, b, d,$	$c, c, d,$	$c, d, d,$	$d, a, d,$	$d, b, d,$	$d, c, d,$	$d, d, d.$

The mean of the 64 sample means is

$$\frac{1}{64}\left(\frac{a+a+a}{3}+\frac{a+a+b}{3}+\ldots+\frac{d+d+d}{3}\right)$$

In this expression there are 64×3 values of the variate, so each of a, b, c, d occurs $\dfrac{64 \times 3}{4}$ times. Therefore the mean of the sample means is $\frac{1}{4}(a+b+c+d)$, which equals μ, the mean of the population.

We can now write down by **(7)** the variance of the population

$$\sigma^2 = \frac{\sum_p (x-\mu)^2}{4}$$

where $\sum_p$ denotes a summation over the population. Further we can also write down by **(7)** the variance of the distribution of means

$$\sigma_m^2 = \frac{\sum_s (m-\mu)^2}{64}$$

where $\sum_s$ denotes a summation over the 64 samples and m is the mean of a sample. Now if x_1, x_2, x_3, are the values of the variate in a sample *in order*,

$$\sigma_m^2 = \frac{1}{64}\sum_s\left(\frac{x_1+x_2+x_3}{3}-\mu\right)^2$$

$$= \frac{1}{64\times 9}\sum_s \{(x_1-\mu)+(x_2-\mu)+(x_3-\mu)\}^2$$

$$= \frac{1}{64\times 9}\sum_s \{(x_1-\mu)^2+(x_2-\mu)^2+(x_3-\mu)^2\}+R^*$$

where

$$R = \frac{2}{64\times 9}\sum_s \{(x_1-\mu)(x_2-\mu)\} \text{ and similar terms in } x_2, x_3 \text{ and } x_3, x_1.$$

* This line follows from the one above by the identity
$$(p+q+r)^2 = p^2+q^2+r^2+2pq+2qr+2rp.$$

We now have to show that $R=0$, so consider the expression

$$\Sigma_s \{(x_1-\mu)(x_2-\mu)\}$$

Each value of x is paired 4 times with each value of x in the population (see the list above and remember that we are dealing only with the first pair in each sample), so that

$$\Sigma_s \{(x_1-\mu)(x_2-\mu)\} = 4(a-\mu) \Sigma_p (x-\mu) + 4(b-\mu) \Sigma_p (x-\mu)$$
$$+ 4(c-\mu) \Sigma_p (x-\mu) + 4(d-\mu) \Sigma_p (x-\mu)$$

But $\Sigma_p (x-\mu)=0$ (by (4b)) therefore $\Sigma_s \{(x_1-\mu)(x_2-\mu)\}=0$ and likewise for the similar expressions in x_2, x_3 and x_3, x_1. Hence $R=0$. Therefore

$$\sigma_m^2 = \frac{1}{64 \times 9} \sum_s \{(x_1-\mu)^2 + (x_2-\mu)^2 + (x_3-\mu)^2\}$$

Now each of the 4 values of x is repeated 16 times in each position of the sample therefore

$$\sigma_m^2 = \frac{16}{64 \times 9} \sum_p \{(x-\mu)^2 + (x-\mu)^2 + (x-\mu)^2\}$$

$$= \frac{1}{9} \times 3 \frac{\Sigma_p (x-\mu)^2}{4}$$

$$\therefore \sigma_m^2 = \frac{\sigma^2}{3}$$

This proves the particular case of the theorem when there are 4 values of the variate and the sample is of size 3. If you have followed the proof, the general case should not present difficulty. We shall restrict ourselves to a finite population, which is usually what we are concerned with.

Let

μ be the mean of the population,

m_i be the mean of a sample,

ν be the number of values of the variate in the population,

N be the number of possible samples of size n, order being considered,

σ be the standard deviation of the population,

σ_m be the standard deviation (standard error) of the distribution of means, and let Σ_p and Σ_s denote summations over the population and samples respectively.

The mean of the distribution of means is

$$\frac{1}{N}(m_1 + m_2 + \ldots + m_N)$$

There are nN values of the variate in this expression, so each is repeated nN/v times. Therefore the mean of the distribution of means is

$$\frac{1}{N}\cdot\frac{nN}{v}\frac{\sum_\mathrm{p} x}{n} = \frac{\sum_\mathrm{p} x}{v} = \mu \qquad \text{(by (4))}$$

Now by (7)

$$\sigma^2 = \frac{\sum_\mathrm{p} (x-\mu)^2}{v}$$

and

$$\sigma_m^2 = \frac{\sum_\mathrm{s} (m_i-\mu)^2}{N}$$

Let $x_1, x_2, \ldots, x_n$ be the values of the variate in a sample, taken in order, then

$$\sigma_m^2 = \frac{1}{N}\sum_\mathrm{s} \left(\frac{x_1+x_2+\ldots+x_n}{n}-\mu\right)^2$$

$$= \frac{1}{Nn^2}\sum_\mathrm{s} \{(x_1-\mu)+(x_2-\mu)+\ldots+(x_n-\mu)\}^2$$

$$= \frac{1}{Nn^2}\sum_\mathrm{s} \{(x_1-\mu)^2+(x_2-\mu)^2+\ldots+(x_n-\mu)^2\}+R$$

where $\quad R = \dfrac{2}{Nn^2}\displaystyle\sum_\mathrm{s} (x_1-\mu)(x_2-\mu)$ and similar terms

Each value of x_1 occurs an equal number of times (since we consider every possible sample), so that $\sum_\mathrm{s} (x_1-\mu)(x_2-\mu)$ is some multiple of

$$\sum_\mathrm{p} \{(x-\mu)\sum_\mathrm{p} (x-\mu)\}$$

But $\sum_\mathrm{p} (x-\mu)=0$ (by (4b)), so $\sum_\mathrm{s} (x_1-\mu)(x_2-\mu)=0$ and hence $R=0$.

$$\therefore \sigma_m^2 = \frac{1}{Nn^2}\sum_\mathrm{s} \{(x_1-\mu)^2+(x_2-\mu)^2+\ldots+(x_n-\mu)^2\}$$

Now $\sum_\mathrm{s} (x_i-\mu)^2$ contains N terms; each value of the v values of the variate in the population appears an equal number of times, so

$$\sum_\mathrm{s} (x_i-\mu)^2 = \frac{N}{v}\sum_\mathrm{p} (x-\mu)^2$$

$$\therefore \sigma_m^2 = \frac{1}{Nn^2}\cdot\frac{nN}{v}\sum_\mathrm{p} (x-\mu)^2$$

$$= \frac{1}{n}\cdot\frac{\sum_\mathrm{p} (x-\mu)^2}{v}$$

$$\therefore \sigma_m^2 = \frac{\sigma^2}{n}$$

Notice the complete generality of this theorem: we have had to make no assumption about the nature of the population (except that it is finite) and there is no restriction on the magnitude of n. It is worth noticing, too, that the value of the theorem is enhanced by the fact that the standard error of the distribution of means does not in any way depend on the mean of this distribution—only on its standard deviation and on the size of the sample.

The problem of finding the variation that can be expected in the value of the mean of a sample is now 'half' solved; we shall consider the other part of the problem—the form of the distribution of means—in the next section.

Exercise 5d

1. For a given population, how does the standard error of the mean vary with the size of the sample?

2. Refer back to the experiment of §5.2, p. 70, and Exercise 5a, No. 1. What is the standard error of the theoretical distribution of means? Compare it with the standard deviation of the experimental distribution.

3. Find the standard deviations of the theoretical distributions of: (i) the score when one die is thrown, (ii) the score when two dice are thrown together. Deduce the standard error of the mean score when two dice are thrown together from each of the standard deviations found already and check that the answers are the same.

Distribution of means

5.7. We showed in the last section that if simple samples of size n are taken from a population with standard deviation σ, the standard error (i.e. standard deviation) of the distribution of means of the samples is $\sigma/\sqrt{n}$. The theorem is completely general but some assumption has to be made about the nature of the population before a sampling distribution of the mean can be found. For a normal* population it can be proved (see Chapter 9) that the distribution of means is also normal.

The method of Chapter 9 only covers normal distributions; for others we can, however, appeal to the Central Limit Theorem, whose proof lies outside the scope of this book. This theorem states that under certain conditions (satisfied under the present circumstances), if y is the sum of n independent random variates, then $z = \dfrac{y - \bar{y}}{\sigma_y}$ approaches the normal form as $n \to \infty$, where $\bar{y}$, σ_y are the mean and standard deviation of the sum.

---

* Remember that, throughout this and the following chapters, 'normal' is a technical term referring to the normal distribution.

Fig. 5.2 illustrates this limiting process; y is taken to be the sum of the scores when n dice are thrown together (the scores on the individual dice being independent random variates). For sake of comparison, the probabilities of the various values of y have been plotted against $z = \dfrac{y - \bar{y}}{\sigma_y}$; the scale on the vertical axis has, accordingly, been increased by a factor of σ_y. Clearly, with $n=4$, the limiting process has not gone far but the similarity to the normal distribution is already quite close.

From the Central Limit Theorem it follows that the mean of n such variates is normally distributed (but with standard deviation $\sigma_y/\sqrt{n}$). The accuracy of the approximation to the normal distribution will depend on the population and on n—the greater the departure of the population from normal, the greater should n be before probabilities are calculated from the normal distribution function.

A good example of a population which is not normal is the age distribution of the inhabitants of the British Isles; another is the rectangular distribution, for instance the one considered in the experiment of §5.2; nor would it be advisable to assume a normal distribution of means if the population curve had two maxima.

As to the magnitude of n, the nearer the population is to normal, the smaller is it safe to take it. One trouble is that it is not usually known how the population is distributed; after all, samples are usually taken to find something out about the population. If the sample is very nearly normal, n may be as low as 50, but 100 is safer; for a noticeably asymmetrical distribution it would be wise to take n to be 250 or more.

Example 3. *The achievement in English and arithmetic of pupils in junior schools is often assessed by means of tests standardised with mean* 100, *standard deviation* 15, *and having a normal distribution. If* 120 *pupils in a junior school have a mean score of* 103 *on one such test, could this excess over* 100 *be attributed to chance?*

The standard deviation of the population is 15. Therefore the standard error of the mean of samples of size 120 is $15/\sqrt{120}$.

The deviation of 103 from the mean of the population $103 - 100 = 3$. Hence the critical ratio

$$\frac{\text{deviation}}{\text{standard error}} = \frac{3}{15/\sqrt{120}} = \frac{\sqrt{120}}{5} = 2 \cdot 190$$

The corresponding normal probability (Table A) is 0·9857, so the probability of a deviation greater than 3 is 0·0143, Hence the probability of a deviation numerically greater than 3 is $2 \times 0 \cdot 0143 = 0 \cdot 0286$, or about 1 in 35.

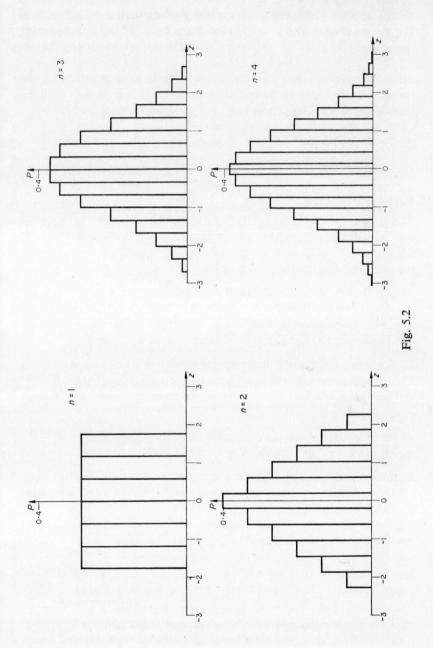

Fig. 5.2

This is as far as the statistics takes us; a consideration of things such as results in other years, the quality of the pupils entering the school, and the standard of teaching, might discover a cause of the above-average mean, but it is not out of the question that it should have arisen by chance.

Note. In practice, samples are seldom simple, as is assumed by the theorem on p. 81. If we do not allow an individual to be drawn more than once, it may be shown that, with the notation of p. 83,

$$\sigma_m{}^2 = \frac{\sigma^2 (\nu - n)}{n (\nu - 1)}.$$

If ν is large compared with n, (19) provides a satisfactory approximation.

Exercise 5e

1. Sketch the normal probability curve (scales on both axes 1 in. to 1 unit) and with the same axes sketch the sampling distribution of means of samples of 100 taken from the normal distribution. (*Note*: The area under the sampling distribution must be 1.)

2. In a factory, the mean length of a certain component is 0·9000 in., the standard deviation is 0·0015 in. and the distribution is normal. If the mean length of 50 components made by a particular worker is 0·9005 in., should this be regarded as significant?

3. For a normally distributed population of heights of men with mean 67 in. and standard deviation 2·5 in., find the probability that a sample of 100 heights should have a mean differing by more than $\frac{1}{2}$ in. from the mean of the population.

4. With the data of Example 3, within what limits would you expect the means of 99 per cent of random samples of 120 children to lie?

5. If 12 dice are thrown together and a score greater than 3 on any die is counted a success, write down the mean and standard deviation of the probability distribution of the number of successes.

Twelve dice were thrown together 4096 times and the following distribution of successes was obtained:

No. of successes	0	1	2	3	4	5	6	7	8	9	10	11	12
Frequency	0	10	56	192	449	785	912	802	534	263	84	9	0

Discuss whether the mean of this experimental distribution differs significantly from the theoretical mean. (Calculated from Weldon's data quoted in *Encyclopaedia Britannica*, 11th edn 22, 394.)

CHAPTER 6

Introduction to correlation

6.1. Do fat fathers have fat sons? Are people with big heads brainy? Does cigarette smoking cause lung cancer? Problems of this sort can be tackled by means of the correlation coefficient which we are introducing in this chapter. The idea behind correlation is very familiar to us: we expect husbands and wives to be fairly close in age; we should be surprised if a tall couple had a very short child; taller people tend to be heavier than short people. All this, however, is vague. None of the statements that have been made in this paragraph has the precision of an equation, nor should we expect it, but we have no means of telling whether the ages of husband and wife are more or less closely associated than people's heights and weights. What we are wanting, then, is a measure of the closeness of the association between two variates.

I have here a list of the heights and weights of all the boys in one year of a local direct grant grammar school—95 pairs of heights and weights at the beginning of the autumn term 1963. Just as we found a graphical representation of the distribution of yeast cells helpful in §2.4, so here we shall make use of what is called a *scatter diagram*. On the x-axis we shall read off height and on the y-axis weight so that, given the height and weight of any boy in the year, we can put a cross at the corresponding point of the graph. This has been done for the heights and weights of the 95 boys in Fig. 6.1. As we would expect, there are no very tall boys who are very light, nor very heavy boys who are very short; it is in fact the absence of these that tells us the heights and weights are correlated (for a reservation about this statement, see below) and on this observation we shall build our approach to the correlation coefficient.

In Fig. 6.2 three scatter diagrams have been sketched. (If you like, think of weight measured up the y-axis and height along the x-axis.) On the left there is apparently no association between x and y; on the right the association is very close; and in the middle there appears to be some association between the two variates but less than in Fig. 6.1. Now we transfer the axes to parallel axes with origin at (m_x, m_y), where m_x, m_y are the means of the distributions of x, y (height and weight), and we write $X = x - m_x$, $Y = y - m_y$. See Fig. 6.3.

Remember that the scatter diagram on the right of Fig. 6.3 has a high degree of association, or correlation, between x and y, and that the scatter diagram on the left has very little, if any. We want, then, some measure that will express this idea. Notice that on the right the second and fourth quadrants are nearly empty and recall that the product XY is negative in

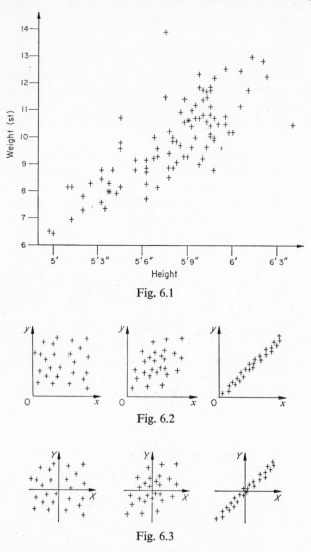

Fig. 6.1

Fig. 6.2

Fig. 6.3

these quadrants and positive in the first and third. If, then, we took $\sum XY$ as a measure of correlation between the variates x and y, it would be zero, or nearly zero, for the scatter diagram on the left, positive for the one in the middle and larger and positive for that on the right. So far, so good, but we can easily increase $\sum XY$ by taking further pairs of values of x and y; it appears advisable, therefore, to take the mean value $\sum XY/n$. However, before you think this is our final measure of correlation, here is a further snag. If a Frenchman had weighed the 95 boys referred to at the beginning of the chapter, he would have used kilogrammes and, if he had measured their heights, he would have used centimetres. Clearly it is unsatisfactory to have the measure of correlation depending on the units of measurement and something has to be done about it—some sort of standard units are needed. This fortunately is very easily provided: if s_x is the standard deviation of x, the ratio $(x-m_x)/s_x$ is independent of the units used, so we define the *correlation coefficient* r by the formula

$$\frac{\sum \dfrac{XY}{s_x s_y}}{n}$$

$$\therefore r = \frac{\dfrac{1}{n}\sum (x-m_x)(y-m_y)}{s_x s_y} \tag{20}$$

where s_x, s_y are the standard deviations of x and y respectively.

The symbol r was introduced by Galton in 1877 but it was not until 1888 that he defined correlation and explained how to calculate r. The reasons for the choice of symbol and for this delay will be given in Chapter 9. r can take values in the range $-1 \leqslant r \leqslant +1$ (see Exercise 6a, Nos. 5 and 6); the meaning to be attributed to negative values is discussed below. While the correlation coefficient defined above is probably the most frequently used, it is not always appropriate—some attention will be paid to this point in Chapter 9.

Example 1. *Calculate r for the pairs of x and y below.*

$$x \quad 1 \quad 4 \quad 5 \quad 6 \quad 9$$
$$y \quad 2 \quad 5 \quad 6 \quad 8 \quad 9$$

To begin with we need m_x and m_y, then we shall need s_x and s_y.

$$\sum x = 25, \quad n = 5. \qquad \therefore m_x = 5.$$
$$\sum y = 30, \quad n = 5. \qquad \therefore m_y = 6.$$

x	y	$x-m_x$	$y-m_y$	$(x-m_x)^2$	$(y-m_y)^2$	$(x-m_x)(y-m_y)$
1	2	-4	-4	16	16	16
4	5	-1	-1	1	1	1
5	6	0	0	0	0	0
6	8	1	2	1	4	2
9	9	4	3	16	9	12
$\overline{25}$	$\overline{30}$			$\overline{34}$	$\overline{30}$	$\overline{31}$

$$s_x = \sqrt{\frac{\sum (x - m_x)^2}{n}} = \sqrt{\frac{34}{5}} \qquad \text{by (7)}$$

$$s_y = \sqrt{\frac{\sum (y - m_y)^2}{n}} = \sqrt{\frac{30}{5}} \qquad \text{by (7)}$$

$$\therefore r = \frac{\dfrac{1}{n} \sum (x - m_x)(y - m_y)}{s_x s_y} = \frac{\dfrac{31}{5}}{\sqrt{\dfrac{34}{5}}\sqrt{\dfrac{30}{5}}} = 0\!\cdot\!97$$

It sometimes happens that, as one variate increases, another decreases; for instance between 1938 and 1949, as average weekly earnings in the United Kingdom increased, the number of trade unions decreased. (*Annual abstract of statistics*, No. 87, H.M.S.O.).

Year	1938	1941	1942	1943	1944	1945	1946	1947	1948	1949
No. of trade unions	1024	996	991	987	963	781	753	733	706	706
Average weekly earnings	69	99	111	121	124	121	121	128	143	146

(men aged 21 and over) to nearest shilling

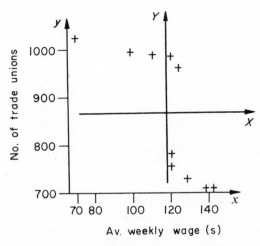

Fig. 6.4

X and *Y* axes have been drawn through (m_x, m_y) as previously and it will be noticed that most of the points on the scatter diagram fall in the second and fourth quadrants so that $\sum XY$, and hence *r*, will be negative—it turns out that $r = -0.74$. Just as in coordinate geometry a negative gradient shows that one variable decreases as the other increases, so a negative correlation coefficient is an indication that larger values of one variate are associated with smaller values of the other variate.

As with tests of significance (see p. 75), we cannot conclude that the decline in the number of trade unions was the *cause* of the increase in average weekly wage nor, indeed, the converse: the interpretation of the correlation is a matter for an economist. In fact it is quite easy to find similar examples of coincidental correlation when two variates increase or decrease with time.

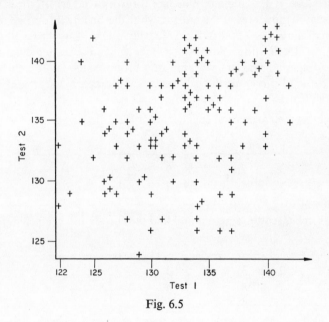

Fig. 6.5

The importance to be attached to the magnitude of a correlation coefficient depends on the circumstances of the case. When standardised tests of English, arithmetic and 'intelligence' are used for secondary selection at 11, correlations of over 0·9 are to be expected if the candidates take two equivalent forms of the *same* test within a few weeks—here we are dealing with the whole ability range. On the other hand Fig. 6.5 shows the scatter diagram for the scores at 11 on two 'intelligence' tests for 119 pupils selected for a grammar school; here the correlation coefficient is only 0·36—the reason for the comparatively low correlation is the fact that only a fraction of the ability range is covered by this set of pupils. The correlation would have been considerably higher had the sample been taken from a comprehensive school. A fairly high correlation is illustrated in Fig. 6.1; there the correlation between the heights and weights is 0·76.

Exercise 6a

1. L. Choose two variates pairs of which can be easily found, e.g. height and span, weight and waist, length and breadth of leaves, etc. Collect pairs of data and display them on a scatter diagram. (If the scatter diagram is prepared on squared paper you may find it easier to group the data and calculate the correlation coefficient later on.)

2. Three dice, red, white and blue, are thrown together 216 times. Let x be the sum of the scores of the red and white dice in any throw and let y be the sum of the scores of the red and blue dice on the same throw. Show the theoretical distribution of pairs of values x, y on a scatter diagram on squared paper. If you are working in a group, some can do this while others actually carry out the experiment and prepare a scatter diagram as they do so.

3. Calculate the correlation coefficient for the following pairs of values of x, y:

x	1	2	3	3	5	5	7	7	8	9
y	3	5	1	7	2	8	3	9	5	7

4. L. Sketch a scatter diagram and find the correlation coefficient for the data:

x	1	1	2	2	3	3	4	4	5	5
y	2	4	5	7	6	8	5	7	2	4

(Here we have an example where there appears to be an association between x and y, but not a *linear* one.)

5. T. Show that if $y = mx$, $(m \neq 0)$ $r = \pm 1$ according as to whether m is positive or negative.

6. T. If $X = x - m_x$, $Y = y - m_y$, show that

$$\frac{1}{n} \sum \left(Y - r \frac{s_y}{s_x} X \right)^2 = s_y^2 (1 - r^2)$$

and deduce that $|r| \leqslant 1$. What happens if $r = \pm 1$?

7. If the correlation coefficient between x and y is r, and s_{x-y} denotes the standard deviation of $(x-y)$, show that

$$s^2_{x-y} = s^2_x + s^2_y - 2rs_x s_y$$

8. T. Show that

$$r = \frac{\frac{1}{n}\sum xy - m_x m_y}{s_x s_y} \tag{21}$$

9. Obtain ten pairs of random digits and calculate their correlation coefficient using formula **(21)**.

Bivariate frequency distributions

6.2. It will probably have become clear to you that it is not easy to calculate a correlation coefficient from the definition **(20)** unless x, y are integers or convenient fractions and n is fairly small. If n is large it is simpler to group the frequencies and to use arbitrary origins, just as we did in calculating the mean and standard deviation, but now we shall be dealing with two variates together.

The table below shows another way of presenting the data of Fig. 6.1 in which a scatter diagram for heights and weights was shown. The heights and weights have been grouped together, just as we should have done if we were dealing with either alone, and the number of boys (or points on the scatter diagram) whose heights and weights lie within each range is recorded in the table below; x and y denote the mid-values of their respective classes.

		Height x in.								
		59	61	63	65	67	69	71	73	75
	13·5					1		1		
	12·5						1	2	1	2
	11·5					1	5	7	2	
weight y st	10·5				1	2	9	12	1	1
	9·5				3	5	7	3		
	8·5		2	6	3	6	1	1		
	7·5			4	1	1				
	6·5	1	2							

The entry 9 under 69 and opposite 10·5 shows that there are nine boys whose heights are in the interval $68 \leqslant x < 70$ in. and whose weights are in the interval $10 \leqslant y < 11$ lb. In the interests of accuracy it would have been better to take intervals of 1 inch in height and $\frac{1}{2}$ stone in weight, but for purposes of illustration the present arrangement is more satisfactory. This table showing the frequencies is called a *bivariate frequency distribution*. A frequency distribution for one variate can, as we have seen in Chapter 2, be represented graphically by a histogram in which the frequencies are represented by areas of rectangles. Analogously a bivariate frequency distribution may be represented by a *stereogram* (from the Greek στερεός meaning solid) in which the frequencies are represented by the

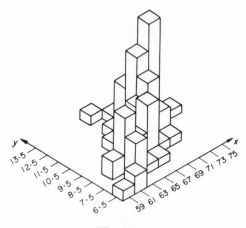

Fig. 6.6

volumes of cuboids. The stereogram for the data above has been sketched in Fig. 6.6. Balsa wood with square section can be used to make a model.

The definition of the correlation coefficient **(20)**, p. 91, is not suitable for the purposes of calculation for two reasons: (i) we shall want to work with an arbitrary origin (x_0, y_0) and (ii) we are dealing with a grouped bivariate frequency distribution and so it is more suitable to bring in f the frequency in any position of the table. We therefore write **(20)** in the appropriate form

$$ r = \frac{\frac{1}{n} \sum f(x - m_x)(y - m_y)}{s_x \, s_y} \qquad \text{(20a)} $$

it should be emphasised that it is the *same* formula as **(20)** only we are saying that any value of $(x - m_x)(y - m_y)$ is to be multiplied by the corresponding value of f. When we were dealing with the standard deviation we found a correction term $(m_x - x_0)^2$ which is subtracted from $(1/n) \sum f(x - x_0)^2$ to give $(1/n) \sum f(x - m_x)^2$. We shall now see what correction is needed to $(1/n) \sum f(x - x_0)(y - y_0)$ in order to obtain the value of $(1/n) \sum f(x - m_x)(y - m_y)$

$$\sum f(x - m_x)(y - m_y) = \sum f\{(x - x_0) + (x_0 - m_x)\}\{(y - y_0) + (y_0 - m_y)\}$$
$$= \sum f(x - x_0)(y - y_0) + \sum f(x - x_0)(y_0 - m_y)$$
$$+ \sum f(x_0 - m_x)(y - y_0) + \sum f(x_0 - m_x)(y_0 - m_y)$$

Consider the last three terms of this expression, remembering that $(x_0 - m_x)$ and $(y_0 - m_y)$ are constants and so they may be taken outside the summation signs.

$$\sum f(x - x_0)(y_0 - m_y) = (y_0 - m_y) \sum f(x - x_0)$$
$$= (y_0 - m_y) . n(m_x - x_0) \qquad \text{(by (5a))}$$
$$= -n(m_x - x_0)(m_y - y_0)$$

Similarly

$$\sum f(x_0 - m_x)(y - y_0) = -n(m_x - x_0)(m_y - y_0)$$
$$\sum f(x_0 - m_x)(y_0 - m_y) = (x_0 - m_x)(y_0 - m_y) \sum f$$
$$= (m_x - x_0)(m_y - y_0) . n \qquad \text{(by (6))}$$

Substituting the expressions we have found,

$$\sum f(x - m_x)(y - m_y) = \sum f(x - x_0)(y - y_0) - n(m_x - x_0)(m_y - y_0)$$

$$\therefore \frac{1}{n} \sum f(x - m_x)(y - m_y) = \frac{1}{n} \sum f(x - x_0)(y - y_0) - (m_x - x_0)(m_y - y_0)$$

$$\therefore r = \frac{\dfrac{1}{n} \sum f(x - x_0)(y - y_0) - (m_x - x_0)(m_y - y_0)}{s_x s_y} \tag{22}$$

If the class intervals in x or y are not 1, but c_x and c_y, we can neatly deal with them by writing $u = (x - x_0)/c_x$, $v = (y - y_0)/c_y$. Now the definition of r was chosen so that it would not be affected by the units in which x and y are measured, so we can calculate it by the formula

$$r = \frac{\dfrac{1}{n} \sum fuv - m_u m_v}{s_u s_v} \tag{22a}$$

This may be deduced from (22) by substitution; the work is straightforward but laborious (see Exercise 6c, No. 8).

Exercise 6b

1. Prepare bivariate frequency tables for the data you collected for Exercise 6a, No. 1.

2. Deduce formulae **(21)** and **(8)** by suitable substitutions in **(22)**.

3. Prove formula **(22)** by starting with the expression $\sum f(x-x_0)(y-y_0)$.

Calculation of *r*

6.3. We now explain a method of calculating *r* for the bivariate frequency distribution given in the last section.

First consider the body of the table; in the top left-hand corner of each of the rectangular *cells* has been entered the frequency *f* from the table on p. 95; we return to explain the other entries in the cells later.

Under f_y has been entered the number of boys with weights in the class with mid-value *y* shown on the left, similarly opposite f_x has been entered the number of boys with heights in the class with mid-value *x* shown at the top. Thus the frequency distribution of weights is shown under f_y and the frequency distribution of heights is shown opposite f_x. We have taken (67, 10·5) as arbitrary origin and defining $u=\frac{1}{2}(x-x_0)$, $v=y-y_0$, the means m_u, m_v and standard deviations s_u, s_v of these variates have been calculated in the usual way, although the arrangement differs slightly.

We now have to calculate $(1/n) \sum fuv-m_u m_v$. In each of the cells containing a value of *f*, the value of *uv*, in italic, has been placed in the top right-hand corner of the cell. Then the product *fuv* is found by multiplying the numbers in the top of each cell and the result is written at the bottom of the cell. The sum of the entries *fuv* for each row are written under $\sum_y fuv$ and the sum of the entries *fuv* for each column are written opposite $\sum_x fuv$. Then $\sum fuv$ is found by adding the column under $\sum_y fuv$ and a check is provided by adding the row opposite $\sum_x fuv$. We then substitute in the formula for *r*.

Note: This is only one of a number of methods of calculating *r* for a bivariate frequency distribution. Another method which is less obvious but which can save labour if many correlations have to be calculated may be found in Exercise 6c, No. 5. Whatever method is employed, research workers using the correlation coefficient need to make checks on the values of m_u, m_v, s_u, s_v. The author used Charlier's check (Exercise 3c, No. 7); some people prefer to calculate these statistics with another arbitrary origin. Don't spend a lot of time doing the straightforward calculations in Exercise 6c: one or two of them should be enough for most people; it is more interesting to calculate *r* from your own data.

Height x in.

Weight y st.	59	61	63	65	67 (x_0)	69	71	73	75	f_y	$v = y - y_0$	$f_y v$	$f_y v^2$	$\Sigma_y fuv$
13·5					$1\ ^{0}$ 0			$1\ ^{9}$ 9		2	3	6	18	9
12·5						$1\ ^{2}$ 2	$2\ ^{4}$ 8	$1\ ^{6}$ 6	$2\ ^{8}$ 16	6	2	12	24	32
11·5					$1\ ^{0}$ 0	$5\ ^{1}$ 5	$7\ ^{2}$ 14	$2\ ^{3}$ 6		15	1	15	15	25
10·5				$1\ ^{0}$ 0	$2\ ^{0}$ 0	$9\ ^{0}$ 0	$12\ ^{0}$ 0	$1\ ^{0}$ 0	$1\ ^{0}$ 0	26	0	0	0	0
9·5				$3\ ^{1}$ 3	$5\ ^{0}$ 0	$7\ ^{-1}$ −7	$3\ ^{-2}$ −6			18	−1	−18	18	−10
8·5		$2\ ^{6}$ 12	$6\ ^{4}$ 24	$3\ ^{2}$ 6	$6\ ^{0}$ 0	$1\ ^{-2}$ −2	$1\ ^{-4}$ −4			19	−2	−38	76	36
7·5			$4\ ^{6}$ 24	$1\ ^{3}$ 3	$1\ ^{0}$ 0					6	−3	−18	54	27
6·5	$1\ ^{16}$ 16	$2\ ^{12}$ 24								3	−4	−12	48	40
f_x	1	4	10	8	16	23	25	5	3	95		−53	253	159
$u = \frac{1}{2}(x - x_0)$	−4	−3	−2	−1	0	1	2	3	4					
$f_x u$	−4	−12	−20	−8	0	23	50	15	12	56				
$f_x u^2$	16	36	40	8	0	23	100	45	48	316				
$\Sigma_x fuv$	16	36	48	12	0	−2	12	21	16	159				

$$m_u = \frac{56}{95}. \quad s_u^2 = \frac{316}{95} - \left(\frac{56}{95}\right)^2. \quad m_v = -\frac{53}{95}. \quad s_v^2 = \frac{253}{95} - \left(-\frac{53}{95}\right)^2.$$

$$r = \frac{\frac{1}{n}\sum fuv - m_u m_v}{s_u s_v} = \frac{\frac{159}{95} - \frac{56}{95}\left(-\frac{53}{95}\right)}{\sqrt{\left\{\frac{316}{95} - \left(\frac{56}{95}\right)^2\right\}}\sqrt{\left\{\frac{253}{95} - \left(-\frac{53}{95}\right)^2\right\}}} = \frac{159 \times 95 - 56(-53)}{\sqrt{\{(316 \times 95 - 56^2)(253 \times 95 - 53^2)\}}} = 0.76$$

Exercise 6c

1. L. Calculate *r* for the bivariate frequency distribution below of the ages of 191 husbands and wives on marriage. For the purpose of this exercise, treat the lowest interval as if it were 15–20 yr.

| | Age of husband *x* yr | | | | | | | | |
	16–	20–	25–	30–	35–	40–	45–	50–	55–60
50–55								1	1
45–						1	1	1	1
40–					1	1	1	1	
35–			1	2	3	2	1	1	
30–		1	4	4	3	2	1		
25–		7	19	9	4	1			
20–	1	46	32	7	2	1			
16–	3	17	6	1					

(Row label: Age of wife *y* yr)

2. Calculate *r* for the data you collected for Exercise 6a, No. 1.

3. L. Find the correlation coefficient for the bivariate frequency distribution of scores on two 'intelligence' tests of 119 pupils admitted to a grammar school. Compare your result with the figure given at the top of p. 94 and explain any difference there may be.

| | Test 1 | | | | | | | | | | |
	122·5	124·5	126·5	128·5	130·5	132·5	134·5	136·5	138·5	140·5	142·5
142·5		1			1	1				5	
140·5		1		1		3	5			2	3
138·5			2	1	2	4	2	4	2	1	1
136·5			1	1	2	4	4	3	1	1	
134·5		1	3	3	4	1		1	1	1	1
132·5	1	1	1	2	5	3	2	2	1	1	
130·5			2	2		1	1	1			
128·5	2		3		1		2	2			
126·5			1	2			2	2			
124·5			1								

(Row label: Test 2)

4. L. The table below gives a bivariate frequency distribution for the gain in score of 103 boys who took two versions of the same test and the original test scores. Calculate the correlation coefficient and suggest reasons why it should be negative.

		Original score						
		0–	10–	20–	30–	40–	50–	60–
	40 to 49		1					
	30 to 39		2	2	1			
	20 to 29		4	6	5	3	1	
Gain in score	10 to 19	1	5	8	7	5	3	1
	0 to 9	1	5	7	6	6	3	1
	−10 to −1		3	4	4	2	1	1
	−20 to −11			1	1		1	
	−30 to −21				1			

5. T.L. Use the result of Exercise 6a, No. 7 to show that

$$r = \frac{s_x^2 + s_y^2 - s_{x-y}^2}{2 s_x s_y}$$

Use this result to calculate the correlation coefficient of the theoretical bivariate frequency distribution below. Red, white and blue dice are thrown together; x is the sum of the scores of the red and white dice, y is the sum of the scores of the red and blue dice. The frequency distribution of the difference $(x-y)$ may be found by counting diagonally (upwards as you go from left to right). (You don't actually have to calculate a standard deviation in this example.)

							x					
		2	3	4	5	6	7	8	9	10	11	12
	12						1	1	1	1	1	1
	11					1	2	2	2	2	2	1
	10				1	2	3	3	3	3	2	1
	9			1	2	3	4	4	4	3	2	1
	8		1	2	3	4	5	5	4	3	2	1
y	7	1	2	3	4	5	6	5	4	3	2	1
	6	1	2	3	4	5	5	4	3	2	1	
	5	1	2	3	4	4	4	3	2	1		
	4	1	2	3	3	3	3	2	1			
	3	1	2	2	2	2	2	1				
	2	1	1	1	1	1	1					

6. Suppose that we have two discrete variates x, y and that P is the probability of the occurrence of both x and y, we may then define the correlation coefficient of such a bivariate probability distribution as

$$\rho = \frac{\Sigma\, P(x-\mu_x)\,(y-\mu_y)}{\sigma_x \sigma_y} \tag{23}$$

ρ (rho), the Greek equivalent of r, will be used for the correlation coefficient of a probability distribution.

Two people each spin 4 coins. What is the bivariate probability distribution of the number of heads obtained by the two people? Show that $\rho=0$ for this bivariate distribution.

If the two people throw 4 dice each, would ρ still be zero for the bivariate probability distribution of the scores obtained by the two people?

7. M. If a number of values of a variate are arranged in order of magnitude, their position in that order is called their *rank*. A common example of this is position in an examination. Let x, y be an individual's rank in two distributions of n individuals, and let $d = x - y$; then the correlation between x and y is called 'Spearman's rank correlation coefficient'. Show that it may be written

$$1 - \frac{6\Sigma\, d^2}{n^3 - n}$$

Use the formula to find the rank correlation coefficient for the following pairs of scores on two reasoning tests taken by 20 students at a training college. (If two scores are equal 6th, let their rank be $6\frac{1}{2}$.)

53 10 62 41 24 15 7 10 54 50 37 27 34 33 31 46 46 18 35 49

60 20 64 33 57 28 28 17 59 54 41 33 51 38 35 56 46 43 47 48

8. Deduce formula **(22a)** by substitution in **(22)**.

Significance of r

6.4. In Exercise 6a you were asked to find the correlation between two ordered sets of random digits. Occasionally r is found to be 0 but usually it is not. Now in the long run we should not expect any correlation between two sets of random digits and so we should attribute any correlation we found to sampling. It is beyond the scope of this book to obtain the sampling distribution of the correlation coefficient and two results are stated without proof; both assume a bivariate normal population (see Chapter 9) for which the correlation coefficient is ρ.

(1) If n is large and it is wished to test the hypothesis that $\rho=0$, the standard error of r, $\sigma_r = 1/\sqrt{n}$, and the distribution is approximately normal.

(2) If

$$z = \tfrac{1}{2}\log_e \frac{1+r}{1-r} \quad \text{and} \quad \zeta = \tfrac{1}{2}\log_e \frac{1+\rho}{1-\rho}$$

the difference $z - \zeta$ has mean and standard error approximately

$$\frac{\rho}{2(n-1)} \quad \text{and} \quad \sqrt{\left\{\frac{1}{n-1} + \frac{4-\rho^2}{2(n-1)^2}\right\}}$$

respectively. A less accurate approximation commonly used is that $z - \zeta$ has zero mean and standard error $1/\sqrt{(n-3)}$. The distribution is very nearly normal so that the normal probability table may be used. This remarkable transformation was given by Fisher in 1921.

Example 2. *Discuss the significance of a correlation of* 0.36 *when* $n = 119$. (*See p. 94.*)

To test the hypothesis that the sample was drawn from a population where $\rho = 0$, we use the result (1) above. The standard error of r

$$\sigma_r = \frac{1}{\sqrt{n}} = \frac{1}{\sqrt{119}} = 0.0917$$

For such a population the mean value of r for different samples is 0

$$\therefore \; \frac{\text{deviation}}{\text{standard error}} = \frac{0.36 - 0}{0.0917} = 3.9$$

Since the deviation is well over three times the standard error the result is very highly significant.

In most practical cases, the procedure of Example 2 is sufficient: we usually want to know whether the correlation observed is to be attributed to correlation in the population or whether it might have arisen through the fluctuations of random sampling. However, if for any reason we wish to test whether an observed correlation is consistent with any given value of ρ in the population, we can use (2) as in the next example.

Example 3. *Is it reasonable to suppose that the correlation of the population is* 0·25 *when a sample of size* 119 *has correlation* 0·35 ?

We write

$$z = \tfrac{1}{2}\log_e \frac{1+r}{1-r} = \tfrac{1}{2}\log_e \frac{1\cdot 35}{0\cdot 65} = \tfrac{1}{2}\log_e 2\cdot 077 = 0\cdot 3655$$

$$\zeta = \tfrac{1}{2}\log_e \frac{1+\rho}{1-\rho} = \tfrac{1}{2}\log_e \frac{1\cdot 25}{0\cdot 75} = \tfrac{1}{2}\log_e 1\cdot 667 = 0\cdot 2554$$

$$\therefore z - \zeta = 0\cdot 1101$$

The standard error of $z - \zeta$ we take to be

$$\sigma_{z-\zeta} = \frac{1}{\sqrt{(n-3)}} = \frac{1}{\sqrt{116}} = 0\cdot 0928$$

$$\frac{\text{deviation}}{\text{standard error}} = \frac{0\cdot 110 - 0}{0\cdot 0928} = 1\cdot 18$$

From the normal probability table we find that the probability that a normal variate should lie outside the range $-1\cdot 18 < x < +1\cdot 18$ is $2(1-0\cdot 881) = 0\cdot 238$. We conclude therefore that it is reasonable to suppose that the sample was drawn from a population where $\rho = 0\cdot 25$.

Exercise 6d

1. Can a correlation of $-0\cdot 17$ be regarded as significant when $n = 103$? (See Exercise 6c, No. 4.)

2. Draw up a table to show the least value of r significant at the 5 per cent, 1 per cent, 0·1 per cent levels for $n = 100, 200, 500$. (For values of the ratio (deviation):(standard error), see p. 79.)

3. If $\rho = 0\cdot 76$ and $n = 95$ find the limits within which r may be expected to lie with a probability of 95%. (Again see p. 79.)

If ρ is equal to the lower limit just obtained, what is the probability that r should exceed 0·76? (Here we have a one-tailed test. Compare the value of the correlation coefficient found in §6.3.)

4. Take n red dice, m white dice and m blue dice, choosing suitable values for n and m; throw all the dice together a number of times and record the pairs of scores x (total on red and white dice) and y (total on red and blue dice). Calculate the correlation coefficient between x and y, and use the relevant test to determine whether r departs significantly from $n/(n+m)$.

CHAPTER 7

Tests of significance II

Difference between two means

7.1. Are English children more neurotic than Canadian children? You may not have thought about this, but here are some suggestive figures on this matter. A test to measure neuroticism and extraversion was administered to 509 Canadian and 534 English children; the scores on neuroticism were as follows (C. G. Costello, and H. M. Brachman, *British Journal of Educational Psychology*, 32, (iii)):

	Mean	Standard deviation
Canadian	5·90	2·84
English	6·30	3·17

At the moment we have not got far enough to be able to test the significance of these results; in Chapter 5 we found the standard error of the mean of a sample but here what we want is the standard error of a *difference* between two means. (We shall also need to know the form of the sampling distribution, but this can wait a little.)

Standard deviation of a difference

7.2. Before we consider the difference between two means, let us tackle the simpler idea of the difference between two variates x and y with means m_x, m_y and standard deviations s_x, s_y. To fix your thinking to something definite you may like to think of x years as the age of a husband and y years as the age of his wife. The argument will be perfectly general but the illustration just given brings out the idea that we shall be concerned with pairs of values x, y. Let us denote the standard deviation of the difference $(x-y)$ by s_{x-y}. Now by **(4a)**, the mean value of $x-y$ is

$$\frac{1}{n}\sum f(x-y) = \frac{1}{n}\sum fx - \frac{1}{n}\sum fy = m_x - m_y$$

105

so by **(7)** the variance of the difference is

$$s^2_{x-y} = \frac{1}{n} \sum f\{(x-y)-(m_x-m_y)\}^2$$

$$= \frac{1}{n} \sum f\{(x-m_x)-(y-m_y)\}^2$$

$$= \frac{1}{n} \sum f(x-m_x)^2 + \frac{1}{n} \sum f(y-m_y)^2 - \frac{2}{n} \sum f(x-m_x)(y-m_y)$$

Hence, by **(7)** and **(20a)**

$$s^2_{x-y} = s^2_x + s^2_y - 2rs_x s_y \qquad (24)$$

Similarly for a probability or theoretical distribution

$$\sigma^2_{x-y} = \sigma^2_x + \sigma^2_y - 2\rho\sigma_x \sigma_y$$

Exercise 7a

1. Find a similar expression for σ^2_{x+y}.

2. What modifications should be made to the proof above to prove the result for two discrete variates whose bivariate *probability* distribution is known?

3. If x is the score of a white die on any throw and y is the score of a blue die thrown at the same time, write down the bivariate probability distribution for the pairs of scores x, y. Find the probability distributions of $x-y$ and $x+y$, and their standard deviations. Why are they equal?

4. L. If variates x_1, x_2 with variances σ^2_1, σ^2_2 are uncorrelated, what is the variance of x_1+x_2? Deduce the variance of the sum of n uncorrelated variates x_1, x_2, ..., x_n with variances σ^2_1, σ^2_2, ..., σ^2_n. Hence show that the Central Limit Theorem (p. 85) gives the standard error of the mean to be $\sigma/\sqrt{n}$.

5. When numbers are rounded to the nearest unit, we may expect a rectangular distribution of errors introduced by rounding. What is the corresponding probability function? Find the standard deviation of this probability distribution.

Use the result of No. 4 to deduce the standard deviation of the error in the sum of twelve numbers rounded to the nearest unit. What is the standard deviation of the mean of the twelve errors?

Standard error of a difference between two means

7.3. Suppose, now, that the x and y of §7.2 are means m_x, m_y of samples of given sizes n_x, n_y (for example, means scores of Canadian and English children on a test); substituting $x = m_x$, $y = m_y$ in

$$s^2_{x-y} = s^2_x + s^2_y - 2rs_x s_y \qquad (24)$$

we obtain (using the Greek letters σ, ρ, now that we are dealing with the theoretical distribution of means)

$$\sigma^2_{m_x - m_y} = \sigma^2_{m_x} + \sigma^2_{m_y} - 2\rho\sigma_{m_x}\sigma_{m_y} \qquad (25)$$

where σ_{m_x}, σ_{m_y} denote the standard deviations of m_x, m_y, and ρ denotes the correlation coefficient between m_x, m_y. Now we can estimate the values of σ_{m_x} and σ_{m_y} by **(19)**, as we did in Chapter 5 (we return to this soon), but what about the value of ρ? Fortunately it turns out that for independent* random samples $\rho = 0$; we proceed to examine this statement.

It will be easier to see what is happening if we take a simple, artificial example, the artificiality being introduced so as to provide an asymmetrical distribution. Suppose we take two dice and, with a felt pen, renumber the faces of each 1, 1, 1, 2, 2, 5, then the various scores for different combinations of the ways the two dice fall are given in the table below.

		Score on 1st die					
		1	1	1	2	2	5
Score on 2nd die	5	6	6	6	7	7	10
	2	3	3	3	4	4	7
	2	3	3	3	4	4	7
	1	2	2	2	3	3	6
	1	2	2	2	3	3	6
	1	2	2	2	3	3	6

Table of scores

From this is obtained the distribution of the mean score of the two dice:

Mean score m_x	1	$1\frac{1}{2}$	2	$2\frac{1}{2}$	3	$3\frac{1}{2}$	4	$4\frac{1}{2}$	5
Theoretical frequency f	9	12	4	0	6	4	0	0	1

Distribution of means

* 'Independent' is used in the same sense as in §1.7. The selection of a particular sample can be regarded as an 'event'.

Now if we have two such pairs of dice, one pair white and the other blue, and throw all four together, we can write down the theoretical bivariate frequency table for the two means m_x, m_y, considering the 1296 ways in which the four dice can fall:

		Mean score of white dice m_x								
		1	$1\frac{1}{2}$	2	$2\frac{1}{2}$	3	$3\frac{1}{2}$	4	$4\frac{1}{2}$	5
	5	9	12	4	0	6	4	0	0	1
	$4\frac{1}{2}$	0	0	0	0	0	0	0	0	0
Mean score of	4	0	0	0	0	0	0	0	0	0
blue dice m_y	$3\frac{1}{2}$	36	48	16	0	24	16	0	0	4
	3	54	72	24	0	36	24	0	0	6
	$2\frac{1}{2}$	0	0	0	0	0	0	0	0	0
	2	36	48	16	0	24	16	0	0	4
	$1\frac{1}{2}$	108	144	48	0	72	48	0	0	12
	1	81	108	36	0	54	36	0	0	9

Bivariate frequency table

We now have to show that $\rho=0$ for this bivariate frequency distribution.

It has already been shown (p. 84) that the mean of the sampling distribution of means is the mean of the population μ, so by **(20a)**

$$\rho = \frac{\dfrac{1}{n}\sum f(m_x-\mu_x)(m_y-\mu_y)}{\sigma_{m_x}\sigma_{m_y}}$$

where μ_x, μ_y are the population means.

Consider the top row of the table; this is the original distribution of means, the mean of which is μ_x. Then, if we denote a summation over the distribution of means by $\sum_s$, the contribution of this row of the table to $\sum f(m_x-\mu_x)(m_y-\mu_y)$ is $\sum_s f(m_x-\mu_x)(5-\mu_y)=(5-\mu_y)\sum_s f(m_x-\mu_x)$. But by **(4b)** $\sum_s f(m_x-\mu_x)=0$ and so the contribution of the top row is zero. For the bottom row the contribution is $(1-\mu_y)\times 9\sum_s f(m_x-\mu_x)$ which is again zero. Indeed each row contributes a multiple of $\sum_s f(m_x-\mu_x)$ and so $\sum f(m_x-\mu_x)(m_y-\mu_y)=0$ and hence $\rho=0$.

If we consider the general case (for a finite population) we shall again have a distribution of means for which $\sum_s f(m_x-\mu_x)=0$. And again every row of the bivariate frequency distribution will be a constant multiple of the distribution of means *because we include every possible pair of means* and so the contribution of every row to $\sum f(m_x-\mu_x)(m_y-\mu_y)$ will be zero and hence $\rho=0$. (But if our method of sampling is not random this will not be so; we return to this later.) Further, the argument will still hold good if the sizes of the samples are different, say n_x and n_y, so for independent samples **(25)** reduces to

$$\sigma^2_{m_x-m_y} = \sigma^2_{m_x} + \sigma^2_{m_y}$$

Now when we wish to test the significance of a difference between two means we do not usually know the standard deviation of the population from which the samples were drawn—this was the case in the problem with which we introduced the chapter—so it is convenient to distinguish between σ the standard deviation of a population and s the standard deviation of a sample drawn from it. This method of using letters of the Greek alphabet for the *parameters* (e.g. mean, standard deviation, correlation coefficient, proportion, etc.) of a *population* and letters of the Latin alphabet for the corresponding *statistics* of a *sample* is in general use. Now by **(19)**

$$\sigma^2_{m_x} = \frac{\sigma^2_x}{n_x} \quad \text{and} \quad \sigma^2_{m_y} = \frac{\sigma^2_y}{n_y}$$

When the samples are large (for small samples see p. 121), s^2_x/n_x, s^2_y/n_y may be taken as estimates of $\sigma^2_{m_x}$ and $\sigma^2_{m_y}$, so for large independent samples we may take

$$\sigma^2_{m_x-m_y} \simeq \frac{s^2_x}{n_x} + \frac{s^2_y}{n_y} \tag{26}$$

Sampling distribution of a difference between two means

7.4. We shall show in Chapter 9 (or the method of proof will be indicated for you to follow) that:

(1) if x, y are normally distributed, then m_x, m_y are also normally distributed,

(2) if two variates are normally distributed, their difference is normally distributed;

hence it follows that if x, y are normally distributed then m_x-m_y is also normally distributed. We do not always have normally distributed variates to deal with, in which case it follows from the Central Limit Theorem (p. 85) that for *large* samples the distribution of m_x-m_y is approximately normal.

So now we are in a position to tackle the problem posed at the beginning of the chapter. If x, y are the Canadian and English scores respectively we have

$$m_x = 5\cdot90, \quad s_x = 2\cdot84, \quad n_x = 509$$

$$m_y = 6\cdot30, \quad s_y = 3\cdot17, \quad n_y = 534$$

so that $\qquad m_x - m_y = -0\cdot40$

Consider the hypothesis that the two samples are drawn from populations whose means μ_x, μ_y are equal, so that $\mu_x - \mu_y = 0$. Now by **(26)**

$$\sigma^2_{m_x - m_y} \simeq \frac{s_x^2}{n_x} + \frac{s_y^2}{n_y}$$

$$= \frac{2\cdot84^2}{509} + \frac{3\cdot17^2}{534}$$

$$= 0\cdot0158 + 0\cdot0188$$

$$= 0\cdot0346$$

$$\therefore \sigma_{m_x - m_y} = 0\cdot186$$

$$\therefore \frac{\text{deviation}}{\text{standard error}} = \frac{-0\cdot40}{0\cdot186} = -2\cdot15$$

From the normal probability table, or the figures given on p. 79, it will be seen that this result is significant at the 5 per cent level. The interpretation of this finding is a matter for psychologists; a statistician would want more information about the method of sampling than has been given.

It may have occurred to you (if it hasn't, you can skip to the next paragraph) that we could have combined the two samples to find an estimate of σ the standard deviation of the population from which it is supposed the samples were drawn. If the two values of s_x and s_y do not differ more than can reasonably be attributed to random sampling, this procedure is all right. On the other hand there may be a considerable difference between the standard deviations of the two samples, as is the case here; if this is the case, can the procedure we have used be justified? To answer this, let us have a quick look back over the chapter so far. In formulae **(24)**, **(25)** we made no assumption that x, y or m_x, m_y were drawn from the same population—it was only in the illustration on p. 107 that we introduced this assumption about m_x, m_y. Now suppose we have two populations whose means are equal but whose standard deviations differ, ρ will still vanish as we showed on p. 108 and so **(26)** will still be valid.

There is a warning which should be given here. Formula **(26)** is only appropriate when the samples are independent, otherwise there may be introduced a correlation between m_x, m_y in the bivariate sampling distribution. This would arise, for instance, if x referred to the adult height of the older of two brothers and y referred to the adult height of the younger; if samples were obtained in this way, when m_x was above average, m_y would also tend to be above average and the standard error of $m_x - m_y$ would be less than it would be for independent samples. Another source of correlation would be introduced by taking two independent samples and then comparing the mean of one of them with the mean of the combined distribution of the two samples. However, if x, y are obtained independently, formula (26) may be used with confidence.

Exercise 7b

1. Measurement of cuckoo eggs laid in hedge-sparrow nests and in garden-warbler nests were reported as follows. (O. H. Latter, *Biometrika* 4, 365.) Can the differences between the means be accounted for by sampling fluctuations?

Nest	No. of eggs	Length (mm) Mean	S.D.	Breadth (mm) Mean	S.D.
Hedge sparrow	58	22·6	0·8759	16·8	0·4970
Garden warbler	91	21·9	0·7860	16·4	0·4900

2. In the investigation referred to at the beginning of the chapter, scores on extraversion were reported as follows.

	No. of subjects	Mean	S.D.
Canadian	509	12·05	3·61
English	534	12·16	3·35

Can the difference between these means be regarded as significant?

3. During an epidemic of Rubella (see Exercise 2e, No. 12) the ages of patients treated for this complaint gave the following results.

	Number	Mean	Variance
Men	174	13·28	112·5
Women	181	14·05	105·7

Is the difference between the means significant?

4. The frequency distributions of birthweight of samples of babies born to mothers under 20 years and between 40 and 45 years are given below. (Butler and Bonham, *op. cit.*)

Birthweight (g)	Under 1000	1001– 1500	1501– 2000	2001– 2500	2501– 3000	3001– 3500	3501– 4000	Over 4000	Totals
Mothers under 20	1	7	12	54	231	390	201	51	947
Mothers 40–45	1	2	7	18	75	129	119	53	404

Can the difference between the means of these distributions be accounted for by the fluctuations of random sampling?

5. The breadth in corpuscles from tadpoles of toads and frogs are compared in the table below. Is the difference between the means significant? (K. Pearson, *Biometrika* 4, 407.)

	Number	Mean	S.D.
B. vulgaris	725	0·01581	0·00186
R. temporaria	1775	0·01530	0·00208

6. In my dictionary, closely related words, e.g.: *cream, creamery, creamy* are given in paragraphs. The object of the following experiment was to estimate the number of such groups of words in the 980 pages forming the body of the dictionary; it is also required to find limits within which the total number of groups lies with a probability of 95 per cent. Make these estimates given that the number of words on 50 pages chosen at random had mean 16·74 and standard deviation 7·421.

7. A group of 68 students at a training college took two forms of a reasoning test and their scores gave the following results.

	Mean	S.D.	
First test	31·0	14·4	Correlation 0·70
Second test	37·4	16·1	

Can the difference in means be accounted for by sampling fluctuations?
    (*Hint*: Use **(24)** and **(19)**.)

Difference between two proportions

7.5. The results of an investigation are often given in the form of percentages—here is a good example in which statistical tests were applied. In the *British Medical Journal* of 1 September 1962, Arnold Brown gave the result of a survey of residents in Cheshire; two groups were taken: one consisted of 409 men aged between 45 and 64 years who died of coronary thrombosis in the period 1 June 1958 to 31 August 1959, and the other was a control sample of size 483 chosen at random from men of similar ages. One of the results reported was that 72·6 per cent of the former sample smoked cigarettes while only 61·9 per cent of the latter did. Is the result statistically significant?

As before we shall discuss this type of problem by using a simple illustration; it is suggested that you should get the feel of what is happening by performing an experiment. I want you to find two experimental distributions for each of which the probability of a success in a single trial is $p = \frac{3}{5}$. These may be obtained from a table of random numbers (or the last digits of numbers in a telephone directory) taking the occurrence of digits 0, 1, 2, 3, 4, 5 to be successes. Or using only the aces, 2's, 3's, 4's and 5's from a pack of playing cards, count ace, 2 or 3 as a success—in this case the card drawn at each trial must be replaced and the pack shuffled before another card is drawn. Record the proportion of successes in 4 such trials and repeat the process a substantial number of times. If two teams are working together they should record their results in order and then the bivariate distribution of the pairs of proportions given by the rth entry ($r = 1, 2, \ldots, n$) in each set should be tabulated as below:

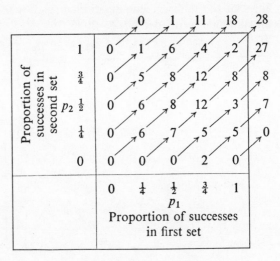

113

Consider the entries 0, 6, 8, 12, 2, linked by arrows along the diagonal; these correspond to pairs of trials where the two proportions were the same—altogether there were 28 of them. Following the arrows either side of this diagonal we find entries corresponding to pairs of trials where the difference between the two proportions was $\frac{1}{4}$, and so on. Writing p_1, p_2 for the proportions of successes in the first and second sets of trials, the frequencies of different values of $p_1 - p_2$ may be seen round the top and the right hand side of the table; for convenience they are copied down below.

$p_1 - p_2$	-1	$-\frac{3}{4}$	$-\frac{1}{2}$	$-\frac{1}{4}$	0	$\frac{1}{4}$	$\frac{1}{2}$	$\frac{3}{4}$	1
Frequency	0	1	11	18	28	27	8	7	0

The theoretical probability distribution can be found as follows. For a single trial, the probabilities of 0, 1, 2, 3, 4 successes are given by the terms of the expansion of $(\frac{2}{5} + \frac{3}{5})^4$ (see §4.4):

No. of successes	0	1	2	3	4
Proportion	0	$\frac{1}{4}$	$\frac{1}{2}$	$\frac{3}{4}$	1
Probability	$\dfrac{16}{5^4}$	$\dfrac{96}{5^4}$	$\dfrac{216}{5^4}$	$\dfrac{216}{5^4}$	$\dfrac{81}{5^4}$

Since any two trials are independent, the probability of any particular pair of proportions occurring is the product of their probabilities (see §1.8), e.g. the probability that $p_1 = \frac{1}{4}$ and $p_2 = \frac{3}{4}$ is

$$\frac{96}{5^4} \times \frac{216}{5^4} = \frac{20\,736}{5^8}$$

The probabilities of the different combinations are given in the table below: each entry should be divided by $5^8 = 390\,625$.

p_2	1296	11232	41688	86424	109345
1	1296	7776	17496	17496	6561	86424
$\frac{3}{4}$	3456	20736	46656	46656	17496	41688
$\frac{1}{2}$	3456	20736	46656	46656	17496	11232
$\frac{1}{4}$	1536	9216	20736	20736	7776	1296
0	256	1536	3456	3456	1296
	0	$\frac{1}{4}$	$\frac{1}{2}$	$\frac{3}{4}$	1
			p_1		

The probability distribution of $p_1 - p_2$ is worked out just like the observed frequency distribution in the paragraph above, only we have to remember to divide the entries in this table by $5^8 = 390625$. For convenience of comparison, the probabilities have been given as percentages:

$p_1 - p_2$	-1	$-\frac{3}{4}$	$-\frac{1}{2}$	$-\frac{1}{4}$	0	$\frac{1}{4}$	$\frac{1}{2}$	$\frac{3}{4}$	1
$100P$	0·3	2·9	10·7	22·1	28·0	22·1	10·7	2·9	0·3
Observed frequency	0	1	11	18	28	27	8	7	0

The agreement is only moderately good but not too bad for 100 observations; you will be able to discuss the closeness of agreement when you have mastered the next chapter.

Now for a test of significance of $p_1 - p_2$, we need to know the standard error of the expression and how it is distributed. First let us find the standard error. We found that, for a probability distribution, the standard error of a difference was given by σ_{x-y} where

$$\sigma_{x-y}^2 = \sigma_x^2 + \sigma_y^2 - 2\rho\sigma_x\sigma_y \tag{24}$$

If we let $x = p_1$, $y = p_2$, and if ρ is now the correlation between p_1 and p_2,

$$\sigma_{p_1-p_2}^2 = \sigma_{p_1}^2 + \sigma_{p_2}^2 - 2\rho\sigma_{p_1}\sigma_{p_2}$$

where $\sigma_{p_1-p_2}^2$, $\sigma_{p_1}^2$, $\sigma_{p_2}^2$ are the standard errors of $(p_1 - p_2)$, p_1, p_2. Now let the samples be sizes n_1, n_2, and let the probability of a success in any trial from the population be p, then by **(18)**

$$\sigma_{p_1} = \sqrt{\frac{pq}{n_1}}, \quad \sigma_{p_2} = \sqrt{\frac{pq}{n_2}}$$

So it only remains to find the correlation between p_1, p_2. The probabilities of $0, 1, \ldots, r, \ldots, n_1$ successes and $0, 1, \ldots, r, \ldots n_2$ successes will be given by the terms of the expansion of $(q+p)^{n_1}$ and $(q+p)^{n_2}$ (see §4.4). If we write these terms as $P_0, P_1, \ldots, P_r, \ldots, P_{n_1}$ and $P_0', P_1', \ldots, P_r', \ldots, P_{n_2}'$, the bivariate probability distribution of the pairs of proportions is given in the table below. The probabilities are multiplied on the assumption that the samples are independent (see §1.8).

			First sample Successes				
			0	1 ...	r	...	n_1
			Proportion $p_1 = x$				
			0	$1/n_1$ ...	r/n_1	...	1
	n_2	1	$P_0 P'_{n_2}$	$P_1 P'_{n_2}$ ...	$P_r P'_{n_2}$	...	$P_{n_1} P'_{n_2}$
Second sample Successes	r Proportion $p_2 = y$	r/n_2	$P_0 P'_r$	$P_1 P'_r$ ...	$P_r P'_r$	...	$P_{n_1} P'_r$
	1	$1/n_2$	$P_0 P'_1$	$P_1 P'_1$ ...	$P_r P'_1$	...	$P_{n_1} P'_1$
	0	0	$P_0 P'_0$	$P_1 P'_0$ ...	$P_r P'_0$	...	$P_{n_1} P'_0$

If P is the probability of the occurrence of any pair of proportions,

$$\rho \sigma_{p_1} \sigma_{p_2} = \sum P(x - \mu_x)(y - \mu_y) \qquad \text{from (23)}$$

where μ_x, μ_y are the means of p_1, p_2. Now in any row of the above table $(y - \mu_y)$ is constant, so that the contribution of any row to $\sum P(x - \mu_x)(y - \mu_y)$ is some multiple of $\sum P(x - \mu_x)$ which is zero (see Exercise 4d, No. 2); hence $\rho = 0$. It should be emphasised that this is so only because we assumed the samples to be independent (cf. §7.3). Substituting this value for ρ, and the values we have found for σ_{p_1} and σ_{p_2}, into the expression for $\sigma^2_{p_1-p_2}$, the standard error of a difference between two proportions in independent samples $\sigma_{p_1-p_2}$ is given by

$$\sigma^2_{p_1-p_2} = \frac{pq}{n_1} + \frac{pq}{n_2} \qquad (27)$$

In view of previous results, you may have conjectured that the sampling distribution of a difference between two proportions is normal when n is large—and this is the case (see §9.5). It is interesting, however, to compare the probability distribution on p. 115 with a normal distribution having the same mean and standard deviation. From symmetry the mean is zero and from (27)

$$\sigma^2_{p_1-p_2} = \frac{\frac{3}{5} \times \frac{2}{5}}{4} + \frac{\frac{3}{5} \times \frac{2}{5}}{4} = 0 \cdot 12$$

Here, then, are the two distributions for comparison:

$p_1 - p_2$	-1	$-\frac{3}{4}$	$-\frac{1}{2}$	$-\frac{1}{4}$	0	$\frac{1}{4}$	$\frac{1}{2}$	$\frac{3}{4}$	1
Probability × 100	0·3	2·9	10·7	22·1	28·0	22·1	10·7	2·9	0·3
Normal probability × 100	0·5	3·0	10·4	22·0	28·2	22·0	10·4	3·0	0·5

The agreement is close but this does not justify us in using the normal probability tables for small values of n_1, n_2 because in practice we very seldom know the values of p (the probability of a success in a single trial from the population). In practice, if we wish to test the hypothesis that two samples have been drawn from the same population we combine the data to obtain p_0, the best estimate we have available, which is given by (total number of successes): (total number of trials)

$$p_0 = \frac{n_1 p_1 + n_2 p_2}{n_1 + n_2}$$

and use an approximation for $\sigma_{p_1-p_2}$ (27) given by

$$\sigma^2_{p_1-p_2} \simeq p_0 q_0 \left(\frac{1}{n_1} + \frac{1}{n_2}\right)$$

Returning now to the data on cigarette smoking and coronary thrombosis given on p. 113, let us test the hypothesis that the two samples were drawn from the same population. We have, using the notation above,

$$n_1 = 409, \quad p_1 = 0 \cdot 726$$

$$n_2 = 483, \quad p_2 = 0 \cdot 619$$

Hence $\qquad p_1 - p_2 = 0 \cdot 107$

and $\qquad p_0 = \dfrac{409 \times 0 \cdot 726 + 483 \times 0 \cdot 619}{409 + 483}$

$$= \frac{596}{892} = 0 \cdot 668$$

So $\qquad \sigma^2_{p_1-p_2} \simeq 0 \cdot 668 \times 0 \cdot 332 \left(\dfrac{1}{409} + \dfrac{1}{483}\right)$

$$= 0 \cdot 222 \times 0 \cdot 004\,515 = 0 \cdot 001\,00$$

$$\therefore \sigma_{p_1-p_2} = 0 \cdot 0316$$

By our hypothesis, the mean value of the difference between the proportions in the population is zero.

$$\therefore \frac{\text{deviation}}{\text{standard error}} = \frac{0 \cdot 107}{0 \cdot 0316} = 3 \cdot 39$$

Reference to the normal probability table (Table A), or the values given on p. 79, shows that the result is significant at the 0·1 per cent level.

Exercise 7c

As ever it is a good idea to collect your own data to analyse; here are two ideas—you will be able to think of others. (i) From a survey of the leisure activities of members of a school, compare the activities of different ages or sexes. (ii) In this country, new cars can be detected by their registration numbers: compare proportions of new cars passing a point at different times of day or compare the proportions on two roads at the same time. (It is well to be elastic about what is meant by 'new' so that the proportion is not too small.)

1. The period of gestation of 3407 out of 8789 boys born in a certain week was less than 40 weeks; the corresponding numbers for girls were 3022 and 8189. Is there any significant difference between the proportions of boys and girls with periods of gestation less than 40 weeks? (Butler and Bonham, *op. cit.*)

2. L. In the survey referred to at the beginning on p. 113, 45·0 per cent of the 409 men who died of coronary thrombosis were 'fond of fatty food' while 55·7 per cent of the control sample of 483 men were 'fond of fatty food'. Is the difference between the two proportions significant?

Of the sample of men who died from coronary thrombosis 28·5 per cent took 1 to 5 cups of coffee daily, while 45·1 per cent of the control sample did. Is this difference significant?

3. In the survey by Butler and Bonham, women were classified as 'tall' if their height was 65 in. or over. The percentages and numbers of tall women in different social classes and in different parts of Britain were as follows:

Social class	% of tall women	Number
Professional	40·9	2162
Non-manual	33·4	1733
Skilled	27·8	6811
Semi-skilled	26·0	4315
Remainder	32·4	1264
All groups	30·0	16285

Place of residence	% of tall women	Number
North	25·4	6022
Central	31·3	5003
South	34·1	5260

Discuss the significance of the different heights of women in the categories (i) professional, non-manual and skilled, (ii) north, central and south. (Don't feel you have to work all this question through—it is largely here for the interest of the data.)

4. In a survey of maladjusted children, 294 boys and 73 girls were found to be left-handed in a sample of 2056 boys and 537 girls. Is the difference between the proportions of left-handed boys and girls significant? (M. L. Kellmer Pringle, *British Journal of Educational Psychology* 31, (ii).)

5. Four pennies and four halfpennies are spun together. Write down the bivariate probability distribution of the proportions of pennies and halfpennies coming down as heads. Deduce the probability distribution of the variate (proportion of pennies showing heads − proportion of halfpennies showing heads). Generalise the result for n of each coin.

6. Compare the proportions of long words (containing, say, more than 6 letters) appearing in random samples taken from essays or chapters written by different authors, possibly in different languages. A number of variates may be treated in this way, or by comparing means, e.g.: vowel frequency in different languages, length of sentences, frequency of certain grammatical constructions, etc.

Small samples

7.6. You may have felt that it is unsatisfactory that we should have had to restrict ourselves in this chapter and in Chapter 5 to large samples. Certainly there are occasions when it is costly to take large samples and we may wish to apply similar tests for small ones, so we turn our attention to this problem.

We have seen in §5.6 that the mean of the distribution of sample means is μ, the mean of the population; this shows that the mean of a sample m is a satisfactory estimate of the mean of the population. This may sound obvious but with the standard deviation the case is different—why this is so, we now consider.

If the population and a sample have sizes N, n and standard deviations σ, s, then by **(7)**

$$\sigma^2 = \frac{1}{N} \sum f(x-\mu)^2$$

and

$$s^2 = \frac{1}{n} \sum f(x-m)^2$$

For the former, the deviations are taken from μ, the mean of the population, but unfortunately we seldom know the value of this parameter—if we

5

did we could obtain an estimate of σ, using the data available, from the formula

$$\sigma^2 \simeq \frac{1}{n} \sum f(x-\mu)^2$$

Now regarding μ as an arbitrary origin x_0, we have by (7) and (8)

$$\frac{1}{n} \sum f(x-\mu)^2 = \frac{1}{n} \sum f(x-m)^2 + (m-\mu)^2 \qquad \text{(i)}$$

To see what value to assign to $(m-\mu)^2$, we shall have a slight digression.

If you went into the empty art room of a school where you knew III B had just been painting and saw an unsigned picture left by a pupil, you would, with the aid of the school list, be able to find the average age of the class concerned. Then in judging the merits of the picture, the best estimate you would have available of the painter's age would be the average age of the class. In formulae

the best estimate of x is its mean $\frac{1}{n} \sum fx = m$.

Replacing x by $(x-m)^2$,

the best estimate of $(x-m)^2$ is its mean $\frac{1}{n} \sum f(x-m)^2$ which is the variance of x.

Replacing x by m and hence m by μ in this last result,

the best estimate of $(m-\mu)^2$ is the variance of m, in other words the square of the standard error of the distribution of means, $\sigma_m^2 = \sigma^2/n$ (19).

Hence we rewrite (i) as

$$\frac{1}{n} \sum f(x-\mu)^2 \simeq \frac{1}{n} \sum f(x-m)^2 + \frac{\sigma^2}{n}$$

$$\therefore \sigma^2 \simeq s^2 + \frac{\sigma^2}{n}$$

Hence an estimate $\hat{\sigma}$ of σ is given by the equation.

$$\therefore \hat{\sigma}^2 = s^2 + \frac{\hat{\sigma}^2}{n}$$

$$\therefore (n-1)\hat{\sigma}^2 = ns^2$$

$$\therefore \hat{\sigma}^2 = \frac{ns^2}{n-1}$$

Alternatively, since

$$s^2 = \frac{1}{n} \sum f(x-m)^2$$

an estimate of σ^2 is

$$\hat{\sigma}^2 = \frac{1}{n-1} \sum f(x-m)^2 \tag{28}$$

A point worth noting is that $\hat{\sigma}^2$ is larger than s^2 because the mean square deviation of a sample is least for deviations from the mean (see §3.5). Of course, if n is large, the difference between s and $\hat{\sigma}$ is negligible. However the improved estimate of σ is of importance in what follows and in Chapter 10.

t distribution

7.7. We are now in a position to discuss the sampling distributions of a mean, and of the difference between two means, for small samples. As in previous tests of significance we consider the critical ratio

$$\frac{\text{deviation}}{\text{standard error}} \tag{i}$$

First consider the sampling distribution of the mean m of a sample of size n drawn from a population with mean μ, and suppose that the standard deviation σ of the population is not known. The deviation of m from μ is $m-\mu$, and by **(19)** the standard error of the mean is $\sigma/\sqrt{n}$. As σ is not known, we estimate its value by **(28)**

$$\hat{\sigma} = \sqrt{\frac{\sum f(x-m)^2}{n-1}}$$

and so the standard error of the mean may be taken to be

$$\sqrt{\left\{\frac{\sum f(x-m)^2}{n-1}\right\}} \Big/ \sqrt{n}$$

Hence an estimate for the critical ratio (i) is given by

$$t = \frac{(m-\mu)\sqrt{n}}{\sqrt{\dfrac{\sum f(x-m)^2}{n-1}}}$$

The distribution of this variate, assuming a normal population, was given by 'Student' (W. S. Gosset) in 1908. If x is normally distributed, it

121

may be shown (the proof is beyond the scope of this book) that t is distributed according to the equation

$$y = y_0\left(1+\frac{t^2}{\nu}\right)^{-\frac{1}{2}(\nu+1)}$$

where $\nu = n-1$, and y_0 is chosen so that the area under the curve represented by this equation is 1. ν is termed the number of 'degrees of freedom' of t. (Degrees of freedom are discussed in Chapter 8.) If ν is large, the curve approaches the normal curve (see Exercise 7d, No. 6), as is to be expected from our knowledge of the sampling distribution of the mean for large samples (see §5.7). Rather than tabulate the integral of the function, it is more convenient to the reader to be given the values that t must exceed for significance at the 5 per cent, 1 per cent and 0·1 per cent levels for different values of ν. These values will be found in Table B at the end of the book. The levels correspond to a two-tailed test of significance (see §5.5).

Example 1. *The distribution of grades of* 20 *pupils from one school in a C.S.E. subject examination are as follows.*

Grade	1	2	3	4	5	6
Frequency	2	3	5	6	3	1

Can this set of grades be regarded as a random sample from a Region for which the average grade in this subject is 3·1?
Proceed as if we are going to find the mean and standard deviation of the distribution.

	x	f	$x-x_0$	$f(x-x_0)$	$f(x-x_0)^2$
	1	2	-2	-4	8
	2	3	-1	-3	3
$x_0 = 3$	3	5	0	0	0
	4	6	1	6	6
	5	3	2	6	12
	6	1	3	3	9
		20		8	38

$$m = x_0 + \frac{1}{n}\sum f(x-x_0) \tag{5a}$$

$$= 3 + \tfrac{8}{20} = 3·4$$

Hence $\qquad m - \mu = 3·4 - 3·1 = 0·3 \quad \text{and} \quad m - x_0 = 0·4$

Now by **(7)** and **(8)**

$$\Sigma f(x-m)^2 = \Sigma f(x-x_0)^2 - n(m-x_0)^2$$
$$= 38 - 20 \times (0.4)^2$$
$$= 34.8$$

But

$$\frac{1}{n-1} \sum f(x-m)^2 = \frac{34.8}{19} = 1.83$$

$$\therefore t = \frac{(m-\mu)\sqrt{n}}{\sqrt{\left(\dfrac{\Sigma f(x-m)^2}{n-1}\right)}} = \frac{0.3 \times \sqrt{20}}{\sqrt{1.83}} = 3.14$$

The number of degrees of freedom of t is $\nu = n-1 = 19$. Referring to Table B, we see that, for $\nu = 19$, t exceeds the values required for significance at the 1 per cent level but not the 0·1 per cent level. Hence the result is significant at the 1 per cent level and it would not be wise to regard this set of grades as a random sample from the Region.

Note: If interpolation is necessary for values of $\nu > 30$, it is advisable to plot a graph using several values of ν.

Question 1. The horizontal displacements of 20 shots fired at a line on a target are found to have standard deviation 0·95 in. If the mean displacement is 0·5 in., does this suggest a systematic error in this direction?

Difference between two means

7.8. The situation considered in the last section is seldom met with in practice. More frequently it is required to test whether two samples of sizes n_1, n_2 with means m_1, m_2 can be regarded as independent random samples drawn from the same population. If the standard deviation of the population is σ, and is not known, the best estimate we can make of σ (see Exercise 7d, No. 5) is $\hat{\sigma}$, where

$$\hat{\sigma}^2 = \frac{1}{n_1+n_2-2}\{\Sigma_1 (x-m_1)^2 + \Sigma_2 (x-m_2)^2\}$$

where Σ_1 and Σ_2 denote summations over the respective samples.

Now the standard error $\sigma_{m_1-m_2}$ of the difference between the means of two random samples is given by

$$\sigma^2_{m_1-m_2} = \sigma^2_{m_1} + \sigma^2_{m_2} - 2\rho\sigma_{m_1}\sigma_{m_2} \tag{25}$$

123

where σ_{m_1} and σ_{m_2} are the standard errors of the means, and ρ is the correlation between m_1, m_2. If the samples are independent, $\rho = 0$ (see p. 107) giving

$$\sigma^2_{m_1-m_2} = \sigma^2_{m_1} + \sigma^2_{m_2}$$

But by **(19)**

$$\sigma^2_{m_1} = \frac{\sigma^2}{n_1}, \qquad \sigma^2_{m_2} = \frac{\sigma^2}{n_2}$$

so that

$$\sigma^2_{m_1-m_2} = \frac{\sigma^2}{n_1} + \frac{\sigma^2}{n_2}$$

$$= \sigma^2 \left(\frac{1}{n_1} + \frac{1}{n_2} \right)$$

$$\therefore \sigma_{m_1-m_2} = \sigma \sqrt{\left(\frac{1}{n_1} + \frac{1}{n_2} \right)}$$

Since σ is not known, we replace it by $\hat{\sigma}$ and take as an estimate of $\sigma_{m_1-m_2}$

$$\hat{\sigma} \sqrt{\left(\frac{1}{n_1} + \frac{1}{n_2} \right)}$$

The critical ratio

$$\frac{\text{deviation}}{\text{standard error}}$$

is therefore taken to be

$$t = \frac{m_1 - m_2}{\hat{\sigma} \sqrt{\left(\dfrac{1}{n_1} + \dfrac{1}{n_2} \right)}}$$

where $\qquad \hat{\sigma}^2 = \dfrac{1}{n_1+n_2-2} \{ \Sigma_1 f(x-m_1)^2 + \Sigma_2 f(x-m_2)^2 \}$

It may be shown that this expression for t is distributed as that in §7.7 but with degrees of freedom $\nu = n_1 + n_2 - 2$.

Example 2. *The boys in the sixth form of a grammar school took a reasoning test with the following results.*

	No. of boys	Mean score	Standard deviation
Arts side	16	27·56	10·58
Science side	29	31·72	13·36

Is the difference between the two means significant?

Consider the hypothesis that the two groups may be regarded as independent random samples from the same population. From **(7)**

$$\sum f(x-m)^2 = ns^2$$

where s is the standard deviation of a sample. Hence

$$\sum_1 f(x-m_1)^2 = 16 \times 10\cdot58^2 = 1791$$

$$\sum_2 f(x-m_2)^2 = 29 \times 13\cdot36^2 = 5176$$

$$\therefore \sum_1 f(x-m_1)^2 + \sum_2 f(x-m_2)^2 = 1791 + 5176 = 6967$$

$$\therefore \hat{\sigma}^2 = \frac{6967}{16+29-2} = 162\cdot0$$

$$\therefore \hat{\sigma} = 12\cdot73$$

Now

$$m_1 - m_2 = 27\cdot56 - 31\cdot72 = -4\cdot16$$

$$\therefore t = \frac{-4\cdot16}{12\cdot73\sqrt{(\frac{1}{16}+\frac{1}{29})}} = -1\cdot05$$

The number of degrees of freedom $\nu = n_1 + n_2 - 2 = 16 + 29 - 2 = 43$. Referring to Table B (p. 189) for $\nu = 60$, it may be seen that the result is clearly not significant, even at the 5 per cent level, since the value we have found for t is numerically less than 2·000.

Exercise 7d

1. L. When an English sentence was translated into German, the distributions of the lengths of words employed gave the following results.

	No. of words	Mean	$\sum f(x-m)^2$
English	31	5·52	790
German	30	7·27	360

What conclusions can be drawn about the average length of words used in English and German?

2. L. At one point of the 1965–66 football season, the distributions of draws in the Second and Fourth Divisions gave the following results.

	No. of teams	Mean no. of draws	Variance
Second Division	22	6·909	6·628
Fourth Division	24	4·833	2·389

Should this difference between the means be regarded as significant?

3. Samples of 10 amp fuses were taken from a machine in the morning and again in the afternoon of the same day. The fuses were blown and the currents measured in amps were as follows.

Morning 9·4, 9·5, 9·7, 9·8, 9·9, 9·9, 10·0, 10·0, 10·2, 10·4.
Afternoon 9·6, 9·9, 9·9, 10·0, 10·0, 10·0, 10·1, 10·2, 10·3, 10·5.

Can the difference between the means of the samples be attributed to random sampling?

4. Two groups were given the same memory task but one was previously instructed about ways of carrying out the task. The scores of the two groups on the test are given below.

Score	4—0	5	6	7	8	9	10	Total
Uninstructed group	0	5	11	9	3	2	2	32
Instructed group	0	0	1	2	4	8	17	32

Find the mean scores of the two groups and decide whether their difference is significant (I. M. L. Hunter, *Memory*.)

5. When the results of two samples are pooled together, the sum of squares may be written $\sum_1 f(x-m_1)^2 + \sum_2 f(x-m_2)^2$. Use the relation $(n-1)\hat{\sigma}^2 = ns^2$ (from p. 120) to find what divisor will give the best estimate of the variance from the combined sum of squares.

6. T. Given that $(1+x/n)^n \to e^x$ as $n \to \infty$, show that the distribution of t (p. 122) approaches the normal curve as $n \to \infty$.

CHAPTER 8

χ^2 distribution

Degrees of freedom

8.1. There have been a number of occasions in this book when we have wanted to compare two sets of frequencies, one theoretical and one observed, relating to the same variate. For instance, if two coins are spun 100 times, the theoretical frequencies of 0, 1, 2 heads are:

No. of heads	0	1	2
Theoretical frequency	25	50	25

But if we performed the experiment and obtained the following distribution:

No. of heads	0	1	2
Observed frequency	23	46	31

we might want to know whether the departure from the theoretical frequencies can be attributed to chance (as opposed to some special skill claimed by the spinner). Another example arose in §4.13 when we fitted a normal distribution to a distribution of heights of 2517 adult male proposers for life insurance.

There are many other occasions when sets of theoretical and observed frequencies need to be compared, a simple instance arising when different treatments for a disease are tried out. The observations might be tabulated as in Table 1.

	Group A (treated)	Group B (control)
No. who recovered	f_1	f_2
No. who died	f_3	f_4

Table 1

Suppose the totals of the columns and rows of Table 1 are as in Table 2.

	Group A	Group B	Totals
No. who recovered	f_1	f_2	270
No. who died	f_3	f_4	90
Totals	200	160	360

Table 2

Corresponding theoretical frequencies F_1, F_2, F_3, F_4, with the same row and column totals, could be calculated on the hypothesis that the proportions of recoveries and deaths may be expected to be the same in both groups.

For both groups together, the ratio

$$(\text{no. recovered}):(\text{no. in experiment}) = 270:360$$

In Group A there are 200 individuals, so we should expect the number who recovered to be

$$F_1 = \tfrac{270}{360} \times 200 = 150$$

and values of F_2, F_3, F_4 can be calculated in a similar way. However, in this case, we can find their values by subtraction from the row and column totals. This fact, which provides a useful check on calculation, is a significant one and an examination of it will repay the time thus spent. Note the following:

(1) Given the value of any *one* of F_1, F_2, F_3, F_4, the values of the other three may be determined from it, using the row and column totals.

(2) Although there are four equations connecting the F's and the row and column totals:

$$F_1 + F_2 = 270, \qquad F_3 + F_4 = 90$$
$$F_1 + F_3 = 200, \qquad F_2 + F_4 = 160$$

any one of these equations may be obtained from the other three (see Exercise 8a, No. 4) so that there are *three* linear equations or *linear constraints* on the four F's.

Now consider another example which might refer to the heights of men in different regions of the country. Suppose that 6000 men from five regions are classified as tall, medium or short, the numbers in each region and each category being given in the column and row totals of Table 3 which contains three rows of five *cells* where the observed (or else the theoretical) frequencies would be recorded.

	Region A	Region B	Region C	Region D	Region E	Totals
Tall	√	√	√	√		1500
Medium	√	√	√	√		3000
Short						1500
	1600	2000	1200	800	400	6000

Table 3

Suppose, further, that we have not decided what hypothesis to test: how many values of the theoretical frequencies $F_1, F_2, \ldots, F_{15}$ (having the same row and column totals as those observed) are sufficient to determine the rest of them? If we know the theoretical frequencies of the tall and medium men in regions A, B, C, D, (the corresponding cells have been ticked in Table 3) we could find the theoretical frequencies of the short men in these regions, using the column totals; then we could find the entries for Region E, using the row totals. Hence 8 suitably chosen values of the F's are sufficient to determine the rest. We express this by saying that the F's have 8 *degrees of freedom*. In the previous illustration, the value of one F determined the other three, so then there was one degree of freedom. In general we may take as a definition: the number of degrees of freedom of a set of theoretical frequencies is the least number of values of these frequencies that is sufficient to determine the rest.

Constraints and degrees of freedom have their place in geometry, too. For instance, a straight line in a given plane has two degrees of freedom: the equation $y = ax + b$ is determined by the two parameters a, b. If the line is made to pass through a given point (x_1, y_1), the values of a, b are then subject to the linear constraint $y_1 = ax_1 + b$. In this case the line has only one degree of freedom, because once a or b is known, the other is determined by this equation.

Question 1. How many degrees of freedom has a sphere in three dimensions? How many has it if the centre must lie on a given plane?

Exercise 8a

1. A treatment for arthritis is carried out with three groups; each group is divided into two categories, 'improved' and 'not improved'. How many degrees of freedom will the set of six theoretical frequencies have?

2. Calculate the theoretical frequencies for Table 3 on the hypothesis that there are equal proportions of tall, medium and short men in each region. (Use the ratio method to find the value of each F and check that the row and column totals are correct.)

3. Three door-to-door salesmen classify their customers as 'easy', 'difficult' or 'indifferent'. How many degrees of freedom will the set of nine theoretical frequencies have?

| | Salesmen | | | |
	A	B	C	Totals
Easy				30
Indifferent				60
Difficult				90
Totals	54	60	66	180

If the numbers of customers are classified by each salesman and the totals are as given above, find the theoretical frequencies on the hypothesis that equal proportions of each type of customer were interviewed by each salesman.

4. Four equations were written down (see p. 128) for the theoretical frequencies corresponding to Table 2. Show that any one of the equations can be derived from the other three.

5. A frequency distribution is formed from the number of calls answered by the fire engines of a certain city on different days of the week. How many degrees of freedom has the set of theoretical frequencies?

6. In an experiment, n trials are made together and the number of successes is recorded. The experiment is repeated a number of times and a frequency distribution is obtained. How many degrees of freedom has the set of theoretical frequencies?

7. n observers place objects in any one of k categories. How many degrees of freedom will a corresponding set of theoretical frequencies have? Can you guess how many linear constraints there will be on the theoretical frequencies? Give a reason if you can.

χ^2 distribution

8.2. We now return to the problem posed at the beginning of this chapter —how to compare two sets of frequencies, one theoretical and one observed, relating to the same variate. We took a simple illustrative example of the distribution of the number of heads obtained when two coins were spun 100 times.

No. of heads	0	1	2	Total
Observed frequency f	23	46	31	100
Theoretical frequency F	25	50	25	100

An obvious way of comparing the frequencies is to examine the deviations of the observed from the theoretical frequencies, $f - F$:

$$f - F \qquad -2 \quad -4 \quad 6$$

However, it is no use adding these up—the sum will be zero because the total frequencies are equal. We have seen in Chapter 3 that mathematicians prefer not to work with numerical differences because it makes theoretical work less easy, so we square the deviations to get rid of their signs:

$$(f - F)^2 \qquad 4 \quad 16 \quad 36$$

Now we ought to take into account the values of the theoretical frequencies because a difference of 4, say, when the theoretical frequency is 25, will be far less acceptable than when the theoretical frequency is 50, 100 or 1000, for example. We accordingly divide the squared deviations by the corresponding theoretical frequency and denote their sum by χ_s^2.* So here

$$\chi_s^2 = \sum \frac{(f - F)^2}{F} = \frac{4}{25} + \frac{16}{50} + \frac{36}{25} = 1 \cdot 92$$

So far, so good, but how can we tell whether this value of χ_s^2 is significant? It is beyond the scope of this book to complete the derivation of the probability function of χ^2 but some indication of the method is helpful because of the limitations imposed by the assumptions involved.

Suppose that we have k cells and that the corresponding sets of observed and theoretical frequencies are $f_1, f_2, \ldots, f_k$ and $F_1, F_2, \ldots, F_k$ then

$$\chi_s^2 = \frac{(f_1 - F_1)^2}{F_1} + \frac{(f_2 - F_2)^2}{F_2} + \ldots + \frac{(f_k - F_k)^2}{F_k} \tag{29}$$

Consider, in particular, F_r; the probability that an individual falls into the corresponding category is $p_r = F_r/n$, where $n = \sum_1^k F_r$. Since p_r is constant,

---

* For the moment χ_s^2 will be used for a value obtained from a sample and χ^2 reserved for the probability distribution.

the distribution of f_r will be binomial and, if n is large and p_r not too small, the normal distribution will give a satisfactory approximation. It is this stage of the derivation which imposes restrictions on the use of the χ^2 test. It is difficult to be precise about 'large' n and 'not too small' p_r but as a working rule n should be greater than 50 and each F_r greater than 10 (but one or two may perhaps be allowed to fall a little below this figure, as in Example 2).

It will be shown at the end of the chapter that χ_s^2 is approximately the sum of m standard normal variates (see p. 141). Now the sum of the squares of a number of standard normal variates is denoted by χ^2, and it may be shown that χ^2 is distributed according to the probability distribution in the form

$$y = K e^{-\frac{1}{2}\chi^2}(\chi^2)^{\frac{1}{2}(v-2)} \qquad \text{(variate } \chi^2) \qquad (30)$$

where v is the number of degrees of freedom of the variates and K a constant.

So we take (30) as an approximation for the distribution of χ_s^2 defined by (29). The distribution of χ^2 was given by Helmert in 1875 and discovered independently in 1900 by Pearson who used it as a test of goodness of fit. The percentage points of this function have been tabulated and are given in Table C. It should be remembered in consulting this table that applications are based on the approximation of the binomial to the normal distribution and therefore should be used with caution. Having emphasised the approximate nature of the test, the suffix will be dropped from χ_s^2.

To apply this distribution to the illustration beginning this section, we must find the number of degrees of freedom of the theoretical frequencies. There are 3 F's and the only constraint on them is that $F_1 + F_2 + F_3 = 100$, so 2 theoretical frequencies must be known before the other is determined; in other words there are 2 degrees of freedom. It should be stressed that we are at liberty to test any hypothesis about the theoretical frequencies and that the binomial distribution is only one (albeit the most obvious) possibility; however *every* such set of F's must satisfy the equation $F_1 + F_2 + F_3 = 100$ and hence has two degrees of freedom. We found that $\chi^2 = 1.92$ and reference to Table C, at the end of the book, shows opposite $v = 2$ and under 0.05 the figure 5.991; this means that, for two degrees of freedom, χ^2 must exceed 5.991 to be significant at this level. Hence the deviations from the theoretical frequencies could easily have arisen by chance. Note that, from the definition of χ^2, (29), every deviation from the theoretical frequency adds a positive contribution to χ^2 so that large values of χ^2 correspond to considerable departures from the theoretical distribution—hence χ^2 must *exceed* the tabulated values for significance at the respective level. This means that we are using a one-tailed test.

Example 1. *The recoveries or deaths of 1765 patients attacked by smallpox in the Glasgow epidemic of 1900–1 are recorded below for vaccinated and unvaccinated persons.* (W. R. Macdonell, *Biometrika* 2, 135.)

	Recoveries	Deaths	Totals
Vaccinated	1493	150	1643
Unvaccinated	59	63	122
Totals	1552	213	1765

Does this evidence support the medical view that vaccination gives some measure of protection against smallpox?

Let us test the hypothesis that vaccination does not assist recovery; in this case we may regard the sets of vaccinated and unvaccinated patients as random samples from the *same* population. We may then calculate theoretical frequencies on the assumption that equal proportions of recoveries and deaths may be expected among the vaccinated and the unvaccinated:

	Recoveries	Deaths	Totals
Vaccinated	$\frac{1643}{1765} \times 1552 = 1445$	$\frac{1643}{1765} \times 213 = 198$	1643
Unvaccinated	$\frac{122}{1765} \times 1552 = 107$	$\frac{122}{1765} \times 213 = 15$	122
Totals	1552	213	1765

$$\chi^2 = \frac{(1493-1445)^2}{1445} + \frac{(150-198)^2}{198} + \frac{(59-107)^2}{107} + \frac{(63-15)^2}{15}$$

$$= 188, \text{ approximately}$$

The number of degrees of freedom $\nu = 1$ (see p. 129). In Table C it may be seen that opposite $\nu = 1$ and under 0·001 there is the entry 10·827. Now our value of χ^2 is considerably greater than this so the probability of obtaining such a large value is considerably less than 0·1 per cent. The hypothesis may therefore be rejected with confidence and we may say that the evidence supports the medical view that vaccination gives some measure of protection against smallpox. Note, however, that there are medical reasons for believing this to be true—the statistics *by themselves* cannot settle questions of cause and effect.

133

Example 2. 0 *and* 5 *as the last digit of a telephone number were counted as 'successes'. The numbers of successes, both observed and expected, in the first 20 numbers in* 100 *columns of a telephone directory are as follows*:

Successes	0	1	2	3	4	5	6	7	8	9 or more	Total
Observed	1	6	17	17	26	10	11	7	3	2	100
Expected	1·2	5·8	13·7	20·5	21·8	17·5	10·9	5·5	2·2	0·9	100·0

Can the divergence between observation and expectation be accounted for by sampling alone?

This time the theoretical frequencies have been calculated for us from the binomial expansion of $(\frac{4}{5}+\frac{1}{5})^{20}$ so we may start by calculating χ^2. Before we do so, however, note that there are five cells in which the expected (or theoretical) frequencies are less than 10 (see p. 132 for the restrictions), so we combine the first two frequencies and the last three. Our table now becomes:

Successes	0 or 1	2	3	4	5	6	7, 8, 9 or more	Total
Observed	7	17	17	26	10	11	12	100
Expected	7·0	13·7	20·5	21·8	17·5	10·9	8·6	100·0

We may calculate as follows (another method is indicated in Exercise 8b, No. 7).

f	F	$f-F$	$(f-F)^2$	$\dfrac{(f-F)^2}{F}$
7	7·0	0	0	0
17	13·7	3·3	10·89	0·795
17	20·5	− 3·5	12·25	0·598
26	21·8	4·2	17·64	0·809
10	17·5	− 7·5	56·25	3·214
11	10·9	0·1	0·01	0·001
12	8·6	3·4	11·56	1·344
100	100·0	Check: 0·0		$\chi^2 = 6\cdot761$

We have seven theoretical frequencies subject to one linear constraint, the total, (so that $F_1+F_2+\ldots+F_7=100$). Hence the number of degrees of freedom $\nu=7-1=6$. From Table C we see that opposite $\nu=6$ and under 0·50, the value given is 5·348, while under 0·3, we find 7·231. Since the value we have found lies between these two values, the probability that χ^2 should exceed 6·761 is between 0·5 and 0·3; hence the divergence between the observed and expected frequencies may be accounted for by sampling.

Exercise 8b

1. The birthdays of 200 boys in a public school were found to fall in the quarters of the year as follows:

Quarter	1	2	3	4
Frequency	60	50	44	46

Is this consistent with the hypothesis that the boys are drawn from a population in which birthdays are uniformly distributed throughout the year?

If you are at a grammar school, try this out for the different months of the year for the pupils at your school. (Some authorities have found a tendency for candidates born in certain months to be favoured by the selection procedure.)

Alternatively, examine the frequencies of cars whose licences expire during the four quarters of the year and test their uniformity.

2. A spinning top for selecting random numbers up to n can be made by drawing a regular n-gon on stiff card, numbering the sides from 1 to n, cutting out the polygon and sticking a pencil through the card at right angles through the centre. Choose some suitable value of n, construct the top and spin it kn times ($k \geqslant 10$, $kn \geqslant 50$), recording the results. Test the uniformity of the distribution.

Supposing you doubled the observed frequencies by spinning the top to a total of $2kn$ times, would the value of χ^2 be changed?

3. 2000 families with two children contained 542 families with two boys, 996 with a boy and a girl, and 462 with two girls. Are these figures consistent with the hypothesis that boys and girls in families of two are distributed in the binomial ratios $1:2:1$?

4. In a classic paper (*Fourth report to the Evolution Committee of the Royal Society*) W. Bateson, E. R. Saunders, and R. C. Punnett, gave the following frequencies of sweet pea flowers of different kinds:

135

Type of flower	Purple long	Purple round	Red long	Red round
Observed	545	25	40	159
Expected on 7:1:1:7 basis	532	45	45	147
Expected on 15:1:1:15 basis	554	23	23	169

Which basis accounts for the observed frequencies better?

5. The frequency of tall, medium and short men married to tall, medium and short women in a sample of 205 couples is given below.

		Wife	
	short	medium	tall
Husband tall	12	20	18
medium	25	51	28
short	9	28	14

Does this set of data suggest that stature has any effect on the choice of a spouse? (F. Galton, *J. Anthrop. Inst.*, 15, 246.)

6. A student (an imaginary one) was asked to throw a die 120 times and hand in the frequency distribution of the scores obtained. He produced the following:

Score	1	2	3	4	5	6
Frequency	19	22	19	20	19	21

Calculate χ^2 and show that the probability of exceeding this value is greater than 0·99. What can you say about the probability that χ^2 should be less than the value obtained? (Here is an example of data that are suspiciously close to the theoretical values: would it be safe to accuse the student of having invented the results?)

7. T. (An alternative method of calculation.) Show that

$$\chi^2 = \sum \frac{f_r^2}{F_r} - 2\sum f_r + \sum F_r$$

and that if

$$\sum f_r = \sum F_r = n$$

$$\chi^2 = \sum \frac{f_r^2}{F_r} - n$$

Re-calculate Example 2 by evaluating $\sum \dfrac{f_r^2}{F_r}$.

8. M. Deduce from **(30)** the equations of the χ^2 distribution for 2 and 4 degrees of freedom.

Sketch the graph of **(30)**, with χ^2 along the x-axis, for $\nu=2, 3, 4$, paying attention to the gradient at the origin and to the position of the maximum. (Since K is different for the three curves, it is better not to sketch them on the same axes.)

The reader should note that the χ^2 distribution becomes more symmetrical as $n \to \infty$. Fisher has shown that the variate $\sqrt{(2\chi^2)}$ is normally distributed with mean $\sqrt{(2\nu-1)}$ and unit standard deviation.

9. L. Show that for the 2×2 frequency table below, where A, B, C, D, are the observed frequencies of individuals classified in two ways (e.g., boy or girl, passed or failed).

A	B
C	D

$$\chi^2 = \frac{(AD-BC)^2(A+B+C+D)}{(A+C)(B+D)(A+B)(C+D)}$$

Check the value of χ^2 calculated in Example 1.

Show further that, with the notation of §7.5, p. 114,

$$\chi^2 = \frac{(p_1-p_2)^2}{\sigma^2_{p_1-p_2}}$$

10. Use χ^2 to test whether the samples of Exercise 7c, No. 2, p. 118, may be regarded as random samples from the same population as regards the numbers in each who were 'fond of fatty food'.

11. When n trials are made and the event has a probability p, the following table is obtained:

	Event occurs Yes	No	Total
Observed frequency	f_1	f_2	n
Theoretical frequency	np	nq	n

Show that χ^2 may be written in the form

$$\left(\frac{x-\mu}{\sigma}\right)^2$$

(Write $x=f_1$.)

12. A 2×2 bivariate frequency table is shown below.

		x	
		0	1
y	1	A	B
	0	C	D

Show that $r = \chi^2/(A+B+C+D)$. (For the value of χ^2, see No. 9.)

Goodness of fit

8.3. In §4.13 we fitted a normal distribution to the distribution of heights of 2517 men requiring life insurance; the observed and normal frequencies are tabulated on p. 65, but we delayed until this chapter a discussion of the goodness of the fit. In the χ^2 distribution we have the appropriate tool but care must be taken over the number of degrees of freedom and we must go rather further into the question of linear constraints. (Note that 'freedom' and 'constraint' are opposite in their meanings—the more constraints, the less freedom.) The case of heights of men in different regions will provide a suitable illustration.

	Region A	Region B	Region C	Region D	Region E	Totals
Tall	F_1	F_2	F_3	F_4	F_5	t
Medium	F_6	F_7	F_8	F_9	F_{10}	u
Short	F_{11}	F_{12}	F_{13}	F_{14}	F_{15}	v
Totals	a	b	c	d	e	n

Here we have 8 degrees of freedom because, once the F's (theoretical frequencies) in bold type are determined, the others may be calculated from the row and column totals.

Another way of looking at this is to note that there are 15 F's and to consider the number of linear constraints on them; 8 equations can be written down:

$$F_1+F_2+F_3+F_4+F_5 = t, \qquad F_1+F_6+F_{11} = a$$
$$F_6+F_7+F_8+F_9+F_{10} = u, \qquad F_2+F_7+F_{12} = b$$
$$F_{11}+F_{12}+F_{13}+F_{14}+F_{15} = v, \qquad F_3+F_8+F_{13} = c$$
$$F_4+F_9+F_{14} = d$$
$$F_5+F_{10}+F_{15} = e$$

But since $t+u+v=a+b+c+d+e$, any one of the equations can be derived from the other 7 (see Exercise 8c, No. 1), so that there are 7 linear constraints on the 15 F's. Now in general 7 unknowns may be determined from 7 linear equations, therefore if 8 F's (suitably chosen) are known the remainder may be found from the row and column totals. This means that in this case we may find the number of degrees of freedom by the formula

number of degrees of freedom

$$= (number\ of\ cells) - (number\ of\ linear\ constraints\ on\ the\ F's) \quad (31)$$

which is equivalent to the definition on p. 129. A similar argument shows that the result holds generally.

The new feature of applying the χ^2 distribution to tests of goodness of fit is that further constraints are placed on the F's; for example, in calculating these for the distribution of heights referred to above, we made use of the mean and standard deviation of the observed distribution, as well as the total frequency n. In the table on p. 65 there are 19 normal or theoretical frequencies so we may write the constraints on the F's as follows:

$$F_1 + F_2 + \ldots + F_{18} + F_{19} = n$$

$$F_1 x_1 + F_2 x_2 + \ldots + F_{18} x_{18} + F_{19} x_{19} = nm$$

$$F_1 x_1^2 + F_2 x_2^2 + \ldots + F_{18} x_{18}^2 + F_{19} x_{19}^2 = ns^2 + nm^2$$

the last two of these being rearrangements of

$$m = \frac{1}{n} \sum fx \ \textbf{(4a)}, \quad \text{and} \quad s^2 = \frac{1}{n} \sum fx^2 - m^2 \ \textbf{(9)}$$

Now these three equations are linear in the F's and so if 16 F's are known the remainder may be determined from them. Therefore the F's have 16 degrees of freedom. Alternatively, by **(31)**, since there are 19 cells,

$$\text{number of degrees of freedom } v = 19 - 3 = 16.$$

The calculation of χ^2 follows.

x	f	F	$f-F$	$(f-F)^2$	$\dfrac{(f-F)^2}{F}$
60·5	0	1	−1	1	1·00
61·5	3	3	0	0	0
62·5	10	8	2	4	0·50
63·5	26	21	5	25	1·19
64·5	53	53	0	0	0
65·5	106	110	−4	16	0·15
66·5	195	207	−12	144	0·70
67·5	301	277	24	576	2·08
68·5	381	352	29	841	2·39
69·5	369	403	−34	1156	2·87
70·5	383	352	31	961	2·73
71·5	269	302	−33	1089	3·61
72·5	186	201	−15	225	1·12
73·5	137	126	11	121	0·96
74·5	54	61	−7	49	0·80
75·5	26	25	1	1	0·04
76·5	15	11	4	16	1·45
77·5	2	3	−1	1	0·33
78·5	1	1	0	0	0
	2517	2517	Check: 0		$\chi^2 = 21.92$

From Table C (p. 190) with $\nu = 16$ it appears that the chance of χ^2 exceeding 21·92 is between 0·1 and 0·2. These probabilities are neither very small, nor very near 1, and so the data appear to be consistent with random fluctuations from a normal distribution.

A word about fitting two other probability distributions. The binomial distribution may involve one or two linear constraints on the F's; if p is chosen without calculating from the observed frequencies, the only constraint on the F's is imposed by the total frequency n; but if p is taken as the observed proportion of successes, an extra constraint is imposed. The Poisson distribution (Exercise 4d, No. 9) involves two linear constraints on the F's if the distribution is calculated from the observed mean—the other constraint is imposed by the total frequency n.

Exercise 8c

1. Show that any equation of the set of 8 in §8.3 (p. 138) may be derived from the other 7, together with the relationship $t+u+v=a+b+c+d+e$. (For the equation including v, for example, add the five including a, b, c, d, e and substitute from those in t, u.)

2. 'Student' (*Biometrika*, 5, 356) gives observed and theoretical distributions of the number of cells counted on the 400 squares of a haemacytometer. Complete the calculation of χ^2.

No. of cells	Observed frequency f	Theoretical frequency F	$f-F$	$(f-F)^2$	$\dfrac{(f-F)^2}{F}$
0	213	202			
1	128	138			
2	37	47			
3	18 ⎫	11 ⎫			
4	3 ⎬ 22	1·84 ⎬ 13			
5	1 ⎭	0·24 ⎭			

The total frequency and the mean were required to calculate these theoretical frequencies: how many degrees of freedom remain? Comment on the closeness of the agreement between the two sets of frequencies.

3. How many linear constraints have been imposed on the theoretical frequencies calculated in Exercise 4j, Nos. 1 and 2? Find the corresponding values of χ^2 and comment on the results.

4. A. S. Parkes (*Biometrika* 15, 379) gives a distribution of the number of males in litters of 8 piglets.

No. of males	0	1	2	3	4	5	6	7	8	Total
Frequency	1	8	37	81	162	77	30	5	1	402

Calculate theoretical frequencies on the hypothesis that the probability of a piglet being male is $\frac{1}{2}$. Group together the first two and last two frequencies; how many degrees of freedom remain? What is the value of χ^2? Comment on the closeness of fit.

Appendix to Chapter 8

8.4. If you look back at §8.2, you might wonder why we took χ^2_s to be

$$\sum \frac{(f_r - F_r)^2}{F_r} \quad \text{rather than} \quad \sum \left(\frac{f_r - F_r}{F_r} \right)^2 ;$$

this should become clear at the end of this section. However, our chief purpose is to show that

$$\chi^2_s = \sum_{r=1}^{k} \frac{(f_r - F_r)^2}{F_r}$$

is approximately the sum of k standard normal variates. The notation of §8.2 will be used.

First we show that $\dfrac{f_r - F_r}{\sqrt{F_r}}$ is distributed about zero mean with unit standard deviation.

What we are going to do is to consider F_r to be given and to examine the sampling distribution of f_r. To do this, we are initially going to remove the restriction which we have made hitherto, that $\sum_1^k f_r = n$ should be constant*. If n varies, it will have a mean value

$$\mu_n = \text{mean value of } \sum_1^k f_r$$

$$= \sum_1^k (\text{mean value of } f_r)$$

$$= \sum_1^k F_r$$

But, if p_r is the probability that an individual should belong to the rth cell,

$$p_r = \frac{F_r}{\sum\limits_1^k F_r}$$

$$\therefore \ \mu_n p_r = F_r \tag{i}$$

Since F_r was assumed to be given, p_r is constant; so the distribution of the number of successes f_r is binomial with mean np_r (by **(11)**), and the mean square deviation from np_r is $np_r q_r$ (by **(14)**). Hence by **(7)** and **(8)**, the mean square deviation of f_r from $\mu_n p_r$ is

$$np_r q_r + (np_r - \mu_n p_r)^2 = np_r q_r + p_r^2 (n - \mu_n)^2 \tag{ii}$$

If we now allow n to vary, f_r has mean $F_r = \mu_n p_r$, and $\sigma_{f_r}^2$, the variance of f_r, is the mean value (taking into account the distribution of n) of the mean square deviation of f_r from $\mu_n p_r$. Hence $\sigma_{f_r}^2$ is the mean value of the expression given in (ii).

$$\therefore \ \sigma_{f_r}^2 = \mu_n p_r q_r + p_r^2 \sigma_n^2 \tag{iii}$$

where σ_n^2 is the variance of n which, by definition, is the mean value of $(n - \mu_n)^2$. Now

$$n = f_1 + f_2 + \ldots + f_k$$

and the frequencies are taken to be independent, so by Exercise 7a, No. 4,

$$\sigma_n^2 = \sigma_{f_1}^2 + \sigma_{f_2}^2 + \ldots + \sigma_{f_k}^2$$

* The method follows that of C. F. Weatherburn in *A first course in mathematical statistics*.

Substituting from (iii)

$$\sigma_n^2 = \sum (\mu_n p_r q_r + p_r^2 \sigma_n^2)$$

$$= \mu_n \sum p_r q_r + \sigma_n^2 \sum p_r^2$$

$$\therefore \sigma_n^2 - \sigma_n^2 \sum p_r^2 = \mu_n \sum p_r q_r$$

Writing

$$\sigma_n^2 = \sigma_n^2 \sum p_r \quad (\text{since } \sum_1^k p_r = \sum_1^k (F_r/n) = 1)$$

$$\sigma_n^2 \{\sum (p_r - p_r^2)\} = \mu_n \sum p_r q_r$$

$$\therefore \sigma_n^2 \sum p_r q_r = \mu_r \sum p_r q_r \quad (\text{since } q_r = 1 - p_r)$$

$$\therefore \sigma_n^2 = \mu_n$$

Substituting in (iii),

$$\sigma_{f_r}^2 = \mu_n (p_r q_r + p_r^2)$$

$$= \mu_n p_r \quad (\text{since } p_r + q_r = 1)$$

$$= F_r \quad (\text{from (i)})$$

Therefore $\dfrac{f_r - F_r}{\sqrt{F_r}}$ is in the form $\dfrac{x - \mu}{\sigma}$ and so has zero mean and unit standard deviation; it is this convenient result which makes it preferable to take

$$\chi_s^2 = \sum \frac{(f_r - F_r)^2}{F_r}$$

rather than the possible alternative

$$\sum \left(\frac{f_r - F_r}{F_r} \right)^2$$

Now we saw on p. 55 that, if n is large and F_r/n not too small, the distribution of f_r is approximately normal. Hence χ_s^2 is approximately the sum of k standard normal variates.

CHAPTER 9

Regression and normal bivariate distribution

Regression

9.1. It comes as a surprise to many people to hear that the sons of tall fathers are not, on the average, as tall as their fathers. The general phenomenon, of which this is an example, was noticed by Sir Francis Galton and described by him in a lecture to the Royal Institution in 1877 as 'reversion'. In a later paper (*J. Anthrop. Inst. 15*, 246) he called the phenomenon 'regression' and gave the following data (female heights have been multiplied by 1·08):

Mean height of parents (in.)

  64·5 65·5 66·5 67·5 68·5 69·5 70·5 71·5 72·5

Median height of adult children (in.)

  65·8 66·7 67·2 67·6 68·2 68·9 69·5 69·9 72·2

It may be seen from the table that children of tall parents tend to be less tall than their parents and that children of short parents tend to be less short than their parents. So the departure from the mean height of a population tends to be less extreme for children than their parents, thus the children's height 'reverts' or 'regresses' towards the mean.

What really surprises people, however, is not that this regression occurs for height, weight or any other particular variate, for which numerical evidence can be produced, but that the phenomenon occurs whenever a correlation coefficient r is observed. Our original example of height and weight in Chapter 6 will serve as an illustration to introduce what are known as 'regression lines'.

From the bivariate frequency table of §6.2 (p. 95) have been calculated the mean weight of boys in the 9 intervals of height and the mean heights of boys in the 8 weight intervals of:

Height x (in.)	59	61	63	65	67	69	71	73	75
Mean weight $\bar{y}_x$ (st)	6·5	7·5	8·1	9·0	9·5	10·4	10·7	11·9	11·8

Weight y (st)	6·5	7·5	8·5	9·5	10·5	11·5	12·5	13·5
Mean height $\bar{x}_y$ (in.)	60·3	64·0	65·1	68·1	70·0	70·3	72·3	70·0

The suffixes x and y have been introduced in $\bar{y}_x$ and $\bar{x}_y$ to stress that these are means of columns and rows with mid-points x and y respectively. The means $\bar{y}_x$ have been plotted against x with crosses in Fig. 9.1 and the means $\bar{x}_y$ have been plotted against y in rings. It may be seen that the two sets of means lie near two straight lines which have been drawn in. Note that the number in each interval is quite small and so the means are liable

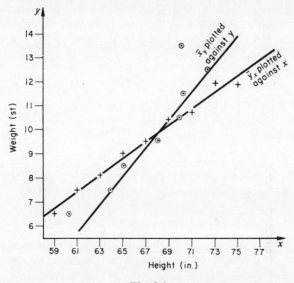

Fig. 9.1

to considerable random error; this is particularly the case for the extreme values, e.g. the means at the top and bottom of Fig. 9.1 are obtained from only two and three individuals respectively. The lines which have been drawn in are called *regression lines*. It sometimes happens that the means lie around *regression curves*: this would happen if, for instance, we plotted the mean number of vehicles passing a counting point against the hour of the day, or if we plotted the mean weight of salmon against their length. In such cases the correlation coefficient r is not a suitable measure of correlation (see Exercise 9d, Nos. 2 and 3). We shall, however, generally restrict ourselves to the simpler case of *linear regression*, i.e., where the means are scattered about straight lines.

The line about which the means $\bar{y}_x$ lie is called the *regression line of* y *on* x; in our present example it represents a line from which we should estimate the weight of one of the boys if we were only told his height. Similarly, the means $\bar{x}_y$ lie about the *regression line of* x *on* y which, in our example, is the line from which we should estimate the height of one of these boys if

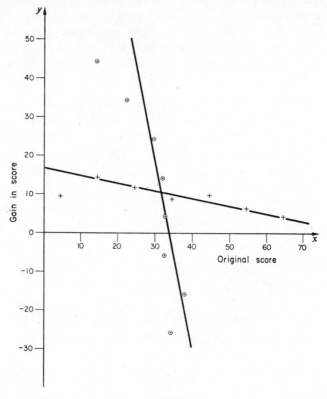

Fig. 9.2

we were only told his weight. To remember which is which, think of 'on' as 'against' so that in the former the means of *y* are plotted *against x*.

Some people wonder why there are two regression lines. One answer is that it is because we can consider either variate as 'independent', in the sense that we select values of it—the other variate being subject to error. Another approach is to see what we find in practice and, if Fig. 9.1 left the matter in doubt, the means plotted in Fig. 9.2 should be more convincing; they were calculated from Exercise 6c, No. 4.

Question 1. Why are the gradients of the regression lines negative in Fig. 9.2?

Exercise 9a

1. 'If the sons of tall fathers are, on the average, less tall than their fathers, and the sons of short fathers are, on the average, less short than their fathers, after a few generations all the men will be nearly the same height—but this does not happen.' Explain this paradox.

2. On weighing machines and in books on diet, you will find tables of height and weight. Do these give regression of height on weight or weight on height? Is the regression linear?

3. L. What are the equations of the regression lines for the bivariate distribution of Exercise 6c, No. 5? What is the value of r?

4. Sketch scatter diagrams to illustrate (i) very high correlation, (ii) nearly zero correlation, (iii) high negative correlation. What can you say about the angles between the regression lines in each case?

5. L. (Suitable for cooperative effort.) Obtain the equations of the regression lines for the bivariate distribution of Exercise 6c, No. 1 by plotting the means and drawing in the regression lines.

Equations of regression lines

9.2. It is natural to ask what are the equations of the regression lines, but before we can tackle this question we must define the lines more closely.

Consider the regression line of y on x. The idea behind this is that the equation of the line should enable us to give $\bar{y}_x$, the mean value of y for any interval of x. Now there are two difficulties about working with the means $\bar{y}_x$: (1) the intervals of x are arbitrary, (2) it would be inadvisable to give equal weight to all values of $\bar{y}_x$ because some will be determined by very few values of x and hence will be liable to greater error than others. We therefore work with values of y instead. The regression line of y on x is taken to be such that if (x, y') be any point on it and x, y are a pair of values of the variates,

$$\sum f(y - y')^2 \text{ is a minimum}$$

(We might have worked with the numerical differences between y and y' but this is not so easy to deal with mathematically as $(y - y')^2$. This is the third time we have preferred squares to numerical differences—see p. 31 in connection with the standard deviation, and p. 131 where χ^2 was introduced.)

Suppose that the distributions of x, y have means m_x, m_y, then to simplify the algebra, let us take parallel axes with origin at (m_x, m_y) as we did in §6.1, writing $X=x-m_x$, $Y=y-m_y$, $Y'=y'-m_y$. Then we require

$$\Sigma f(Y-Y')^2 \text{ to be a minimum}$$

Let the equation of the regression line of y on x (referred to the new axes) be $Y'=aX+b$, then

$$\Sigma f(Y-aX-b)^2 \text{ is to be a minimum}$$

Now

$$\Sigma f(Y-aX-b)^2 = \Sigma f(Y-aX)^2 - 2\Sigma f(Y-aX)b + \Sigma fb^2$$

But
$$\Sigma f(Y-aX)b = b\Sigma fY - ba\Sigma fX$$
$$= b\Sigma f(y-m_y) - ba\Sigma f(x-m_x)$$
$$= 0 \qquad\qquad \textbf{by (4b)}$$

So we require $\Sigma f(Y-aX)^2 + \Sigma fb^2$ to be a minimum. The second term of this expression cannot be negative, so it takes its least value when $b=0$. The regression line therefore passes through the origin, i.e. (m_x, m_y) in the original coordinates.

As to the first term, write

$$z = \Sigma f(Y-aX)^2$$
$$= \Sigma f(Y^2 - 2aXY + a^2X^2)$$
$$= \Sigma fY^2 - 2a\Sigma fXY + a^2\Sigma fX^2$$
$$\therefore \frac{dz}{da} = \qquad -2\Sigma fXY + 2a\Sigma fX^2$$

For minimum value of z, let $dz/da = 0$

$$\therefore -2\Sigma fXY + 2a\Sigma fX^2 = 0$$
$$\therefore a = \frac{\Sigma fXY}{\Sigma fX^2} = \frac{\Sigma f(x-m_x)(y-m_y)}{\Sigma f(x-m_x)^2}$$

$d^2z/da^2 = 2\Sigma fX^2$, which is positive. Hence z has a minimum value. But

$$r = \frac{\dfrac{1}{n}\Sigma f(x-m_x)(y-m_y)}{s_x s_y} \quad \textbf{(20a)} \quad \text{and} \quad s_x^2 = \frac{\Sigma f(x-m_x)^2}{n} \quad \textbf{(7)}$$

$$\therefore a = \frac{r}{s_x^2}\cdot s_x s_y = r\frac{s_y}{s_x}$$

Now we have found that, in the original coordinates, the regression line of y on x passes through (m_x, m_y), so its equation is

$$y - m_y = r\frac{s_y}{s_x}(x - m_x) \tag{32}$$

To remember which way up the fraction s_y/s_x goes; recall how (p. 91) we divided $x - m_x$ and $y - m_y$ respectively by s_x and s_y to make them independent of their units of measurement. Writing (32) as

$$\frac{y - m_y}{s_y} = r\frac{x - m_x}{s_x}$$

we obtain the equation of the regression line of x on y by interchanging x and y:

$$\frac{x - m_x}{s_x} = r\frac{y - m_y}{s_y}$$

or in a more usual form

$$\frac{y - m_y}{s_y} = \frac{1}{r}\frac{x - m_x}{s_x}$$

We can now explain the use of the symbol r for the correlation coefficient. Galton was originally interested in the phenomenon of regression and he arranged that the standard deviations (although he did not use this term) of his two variates were equal. Hence his regression lines of y on x and x on y were in the form

$$y - m_y = r(x - m_x), \qquad y - m_y = \frac{1}{r}(x - m_x)$$

We have seen (Exercise 6a, No. 6) that $|r| \leqslant 1$, and in practical cases $|r| < 1$, so the regression equation of y on x, $y - m_y = r(x - m_x)$, shows that the deviation of y from its mean is (numerically) less than the deviation of x from its mean, and r is a measure of this reversion or regression. It was natural, therefore, for Galton to choose the letter r to denote this measure of 'reversion'.

For the regression equations of Fig. 9.1, we have

$$m_x = 68{\cdot}2, \qquad m_y = 9{\cdot}9, \qquad \frac{s_y}{s_x} = 0{\cdot}44, \qquad r = 0{\cdot}76$$

from which we obtain the equations

$$y - 9{\cdot}9 = 0{\cdot}33(x - 68{\cdot}2) \qquad (y \text{ on } x)$$

$$y - 9{\cdot}9 = 0{\cdot}58(x - 68{\cdot}2) \qquad (x \text{ on } y)$$

The equations of regression lines provide a method of calculating equations of lines fitting experimental data. In practice, experiments at school level hardly warrant the labour involved; however it may well be worth while to calculate the means of the variables and draw a straight line to pass through the point with these coordinates.

Exercise 9b

1. Show that the two regression lines coincide if and only if $r = \pm 1$.

2. Calculate the equations of the regression lines of Exercise 9a, No. 5.

3. т. Show that r^2 is the product of the gradient of the regression line of y on x with the reciprocal of the gradient of the regression line of x on y. Use this result to find r for Exercise 9a, Nos. 3 and 5.

4. Show that both regression lines have the same sign and that the regression line of y on x has the smaller gradient.

5. Show that, for given s_x, s_y, the angle between the regression lines decreases as r increases from 0 to 1.

6. м. Use partial differentiation to obtain the equation of the regression line of y on x. (If $y = ax + b$ is its equation and $z = \sum f(y - ax - b)^2$ is to be a minimum, the condition $\partial z / \partial b = 0$ shows that the line passes through (m_x, m_y).)

Bivariate probability distributions*

9.3. So far we have usually represented a bivariate frequency or probability distribution by a table of values as, for example, in §6.2 (p. 95), but in that section we also indicated that the data could be represented by a stereogram in which the frequencies are represented by the volumes of corresponding cuboids. Now in Chapter 4 we saw how if $\phi(x)$ is the probability function of a variate x, then

$$\int_{-\infty}^{\infty} \phi(x)\,dx = 1$$

and the probability that the variate lies between x and $x + \delta x$ is approximately $\phi(x)\,\delta x$. Similarly, for a continuous bivariate probability distribution given by the function $\phi(x, y)$

$$\int_{-\infty}^{\infty} \int_{-\infty}^{\infty} \phi(x, y)\,dy\,dx = 1$$

---

* Those unfamiliar with double integrals should skip to §9.6, p. 154.

and the probability that the variates lie in the elementary rectangle with diagonal joining (x, y) and $(x + \delta x, y + \delta y)$ is approximately

$$\phi(x, y) \delta y \delta x$$

The equation $z = \phi(x, y)$ represents a surface, called a *probability surface*.

Normal probability: independent variates

9.4. Suppose we have two independent variates x, y, each normally distributed with zero mean and standard deviations σ_x, σ_y. The probabilities that x, y, lie in ranges $x, x + \delta x$ and $y, y + \delta y$ are respectively* (p. 57)

$$\frac{1}{\sigma_x \sqrt{(2\pi)}} \exp\left(-\frac{1}{2}\frac{x^2}{\sigma_x^2}\right) \delta x \quad \text{and} \quad \frac{1}{\sigma_y \sqrt{(2\pi)}} \exp\left(-\frac{1}{2}\frac{y^2}{\sigma_y^2}\right) \delta y$$

Since the variates are independent, the probability of both events is the product

$$\frac{1}{\sigma_x \sigma_y 2\pi} \exp\left\{-\frac{1}{2}\left(\frac{x^2}{\sigma_x^2} + \frac{y^2}{\sigma_y^2}\right)\right\} \delta x \, \delta y$$

So the probability function for the bivariate distribution of x, y is

$$\phi(x, y) = \frac{1}{2\pi\sigma_x \sigma_y} \exp\left\{-\frac{1}{2}\left(\frac{x^2}{\sigma_x^2} + \frac{y^2}{\sigma_y^2}\right)\right\}$$

Difference between two independent normal variates

9.5. We now consider the difference $w = x - y$, where x, y are independent variates normally distributed with zero mean and standard deviation σ_x, σ_y. Our object is to show that w is also normally distributed and so to fill a gap in our argument in §7.4. Pencil and paper would be helpful to fill in the details of algebra—but first try to follow the general lines of the proof.

Fig. 9.3 shows some of the contour lines of the probability surface for the distribution of x, y with probability function (see §9.4)

$$\phi(x, y) = \frac{1}{2\pi\sigma_x \sigma_y} \exp\left\{-\frac{1}{2}\left(\frac{x^2}{\sigma_x^2} + \frac{y^2}{\sigma_y^2}\right)\right\}$$

The probability that w lies in the interval $w_1 \leqslant w \leqslant w_2$ is given by the volume above the domain bounded by $y = x - w_1$ and $y = x - w_2$ (shaded in Fig. 9.3 which shows contour lines of equal probability $\phi(x, y) = \text{const}$. They form ellipses

$$\frac{x^2}{\sigma_x^2} + \frac{y^2}{\sigma_y^2} = k.)$$

---

* The notation $\exp t$ is used to denote e^t; 'exp' is an abbreviation of 'exponential'. As the probabilities are approximate, the argument is not rigorous.

This probability is

$$P = \int\limits_{-\infty}^{\infty} \int\limits_{x-w_2}^{x-w_1} \phi(x,y)\,\mathrm{d}y\,\mathrm{d}x$$

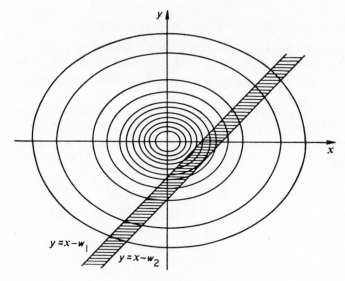

Fig. 9.3

Changing the variable by the substitution $y = x - w$,

$$P = \int\limits_{-\infty}^{\infty} \int\limits_{w_1}^{w_2} \phi(x, x-w)\,\mathrm{d}w\,\mathrm{d}x$$

Changing the order of integration,

$$P = \int\limits_{w_1}^{w_2} \int\limits_{-\infty}^{\infty} \phi(x, x-w)\,\mathrm{d}x\,\mathrm{d}w$$

Now consider

$$\phi(x, x-w) = \frac{1}{2\pi\sigma_x\sigma_y} \exp\left(-\tfrac{1}{2}t^2\right)$$

where

$$t^2 = \frac{x^2}{\sigma_x^2} + \frac{(x-w)^2}{\sigma_y^2}$$

We may now complete the square for x and show by elementary algebra that

$$t^2 = \left(\frac{1}{\sigma_x^2}+\frac{1}{\sigma_y^2}\right)\left\{x^2 - \frac{\frac{2}{\sigma_y^2}}{\frac{1}{\sigma_x^2}+\frac{1}{\sigma_y^2}}wx + \frac{\left(\frac{1}{\sigma_y^2}\right)^2}{\left(\frac{1}{\sigma_x^2}+\frac{1}{\sigma_y^2}\right)^2}w^2 + \frac{\frac{1}{\sigma_x^2\sigma_y^2}}{\left(\frac{1}{\sigma_x^2}+\frac{1}{\sigma_y^2}\right)^2}w^2\right\}$$

$$\therefore \phi(x, x-w) = \frac{1}{2\pi\sigma_x\sigma_y}\exp\left\{-\tfrac{1}{2}c\left(x-\frac{w}{c\sigma_y^2}\right)^2\right\}\exp\left(-\frac{1}{2}\frac{w^2}{c\sigma_x^2\sigma_y^2}\right)$$

where

$$c = \frac{1}{\sigma_x^2}+\frac{1}{\sigma_y^2}$$

Now, treating w as constant, and substituting $u=(x-w/c\sigma_y^2)\sqrt{c}$,

$$\int_{-\infty}^{\infty} \frac{1}{\sqrt{(2\pi)}}\exp\left\{-\tfrac{1}{2}c\left(x-\frac{w}{c\sigma_y^2}\right)^2\right\}dx$$

$$= \int_{-\infty}^{\infty} \frac{1}{\sqrt{c}}\cdot\frac{1}{\sqrt{(2\pi)}}\exp\left(-\tfrac{1}{2}u^2\right)du = \frac{1}{\sqrt{c}}$$

since the area under the normal curve is 1.

$$\therefore P = \int_{w_1}^{w_2} \frac{1}{\sqrt{c}}\cdot\frac{1}{\sigma_x\sigma_y\sqrt{(2\pi)}}\exp\left(-\frac{1}{2}\frac{w^2}{c\sigma_x^2\sigma_y^2}\right)dw$$

But this is in the form

$$\int_{w_1}^{w_2} \frac{1}{\sigma_w\sqrt{(2\pi)}}\exp\left(-\frac{1}{2}\frac{w^2}{\sigma_w^2}\right)dw$$

where

$$\sigma_w^2 = c\sigma_x^2\sigma_y^2$$

$$= \left(\frac{1}{\sigma_x^2}+\frac{1}{\sigma_y^2}\right)\sigma_x^2\sigma_y^2$$

$$= \sigma_y^2+\sigma_x^2$$

Hence w is normally distributed with variance $\sigma_x^2+\sigma_y^2$. This justifies our second assumption of §7.4 (p. 109). Again, it also justifies the use of normal probabilities for testing the significance of a difference between two proportions obtained from large samples (see §7.5).

Statistics

Exercise 9c

1. T. Show that the sum of two independent normally distributed variates is also normally distributed. (Little more than suitable changes of sign are needed in the work above.) What is the variance of the sum in terms of the variances of the variates?

2. T. Use the result of No. 1 to show by induction that the sum of n independent normally distributed variates is normally distributed. Deduce that their mean is also normally distributed.

3. T. Deduce from the results of No. 2 and §9.5 that the sampling distribution of the difference between two means of samples drawn from a normal population is also normal. (See §7.4.)

4. A man and a woman are chosen at random from populations whose heights are normally distributed with means 67 in., 62 in., and standard deviations 2·5 in., 2·3 in. respectively. Find the probability that the difference between their heights should be more than 3 in.

Standard error of estimate

9.6. Most *corps de ballet* have a maximum height for their members, but admission to a ballet school may be made at the age of 9. Here then is a problem of whether an individual girl may expect to be too tall to be a ballerina when she is grown up. With a knowledge of the correlation of the height x in. of a girl at the age of 9 and the adult height y in. of the same girl, it is possible to find a regression line of y on x and make predictions of the adult heights of other girls when they are 9 years old. It is worth asking, however, how much we improve by this method on the lazy method of simply giving the mean height of adult women as an estimate of the adult height of the girl in question.

A measure of the average error made in estimating adult height, by either method, is conveniently available in the standard deviation; for the method which estimates the girl's adult height as the mean adult height of women, this is simply the standard deviation of adult height s_y.

If, however, we take from **(32)** $m_y + r(s_y/s_x)(x - m_x)$ as our estimate of adult height, the mean difference between y and this is

$$\frac{1}{n}\sum f\left\{y - m_y - r\frac{s_y}{s_x}(x - m_x)\right\}$$

$$= \frac{1}{n}\sum f(y - m_y) - \frac{1}{n}r\frac{s_y}{s_x}\sum f(x - m_x)$$

$$= 0 \qquad\qquad\qquad\qquad\qquad\qquad\qquad \text{by (4b)}$$

Hence the variance of the difference is by **(7)** or **(9)**

$$\frac{1}{n}\sum f\left\{(y-m_y)-r\frac{s_y}{s_x}(x-m_x)\right\}^2$$

$$=\frac{1}{n}\sum f\left\{(y-m_y)^2-2r\frac{s_y}{s_x}(x-m_x)(y-m_y)+r^2\frac{s_y^2}{s_x^2}(x-m_x)^2\right\}$$

$$=\frac{1}{n}\sum f(y-m_y)^2-2r\frac{s_y}{s_x}\cdot\frac{1}{n}\sum f(x-m_x)(y-m_y)+r^2\frac{s_y^2}{s_x^2}\cdot\frac{1}{n}\sum f(x-m_x)^2$$

$$=s_y^2-2r\frac{s_y}{s_x}\cdot rs_xs_y+r^2\frac{s_y^2}{s_x^2}\cdot s_x^2 \qquad\text{by (7) and (20a)}$$

$$=s_y^2-2r^2s_y^2+r^2s_y^2$$

$$=s_y^2(1-r^2)=S_y^2,\text{ say}$$

S_y is the standard deviation of the error involved in the estimate or the *standard error of estimate of* y.

We can now compare the standard deviation of the errors of estimate by the two methods:

$$\frac{S_y}{s_y}=\sqrt{(1-r^2)}$$

This ratio shows us the proportion of the error that still remains after we have used a regression equation. For the case used as an illustration, r is about 0·8 and so the error is reduced to about 60 per cent of what it would be by the other method. The improvement may not appear large, but any gain in the accuracy of making predictions is worth while.

To take another example, refer to Fig. 6.1 (p. 90), which shows a scatter diagram for heights and weights of 95 boys. Suppose someone tells us the height of one of these boys, asking us to tell him the boy's weight. We might use the regression line of y on x (Fig. 9.1, p. 145) whose equation is given on p. 149, substituting in the given value of x; in this case the standard deviation of the errors in our estimates for all 95 boys would be

$$S_y\simeq s_y\sqrt{(1-r^2)}\simeq 1\cdot00\text{ lb}$$

On the other hand, we might have been lazy and given the mean weight of the 95 boys every time; we should now have a standard deviation of errors of estimation

$$s_y\simeq 1\cdot53\text{ lb}$$

The ratio of these measures of the error is

$$\sqrt{(1-r^2)}\simeq 0\cdot65$$

so that the error using the regression lines is about 65 per cent of what it would have been by taking m_y as an estimate of the height every time.

Exercise 9d

1. Draw up a table to show the percentage error of estimate still remaining for values of $r = 0, 0.5, 0.75, 0.80, 0.90, 0.95, 0.99$.

2. T. Show that
$$r^2 = 1 - \frac{S_y^2}{s_y^2}$$

If m_{y_x} denotes the mean value of y for a given value of x, let

$$s_y'^2 = \frac{1}{n} \sum f(y - m_{y_x})^2$$

the appropriate value of m_{y_x} being taken for each value of y. η_{yx} the 'correlation ratio of y on x' is defined by analogy with the expression for r as

$$\eta_{yx}^2 = 1 - \frac{s_y'^2}{s_y^2}$$

Write down a similar formula for the correlation ratio of x on y.

Why is the correlation ratio a better measure of correlation than r when regression is non-linear? Explain why $s_y'^2$ is preferred to S_y^2 in the formula for η_{yx}.

3. In Exercise 6a, No. 4, the correlation coefficient was found to be 0. What is the correlation ratio η_{yx} for the same data?

4. M (Normal correlation function.) Consider the bivariate probability distribution with the following properties:

(1) x is normally distributed with zero mean and standard deviation σ_x.

(2) The regression line of y on x is $y = \rho(\sigma_y/\sigma_x)x$ (for probability distributions ρ is used instead of r).

(3) For every value of x, y is normally distributed with mean $\rho(\sigma_y/\sigma_x)x$ and standard deviation $\sigma_y\sqrt{(1-\rho^2)}$ (compare the expression for standard error of estimate).

Write down the probabilities that:
(i) x lies in the range from x to $x+\delta x$.
(ii) y lies in the range from y to $y+\delta y$.
(iii) (x,y) lies in the elementary rectangle with diagonal joining (x,y) and $(x+\delta x, y+\delta y)$.

Show that the bivariate probability function $\phi(x,y)$ is

$$\frac{1}{2\pi\sigma_x\sigma_y\sqrt{(1-\rho^2)}} \exp\left\{-\frac{1}{2(1-\rho^2)}\left(\frac{x^2}{\sigma_x^2} - \frac{2\rho xy}{\sigma_x\sigma_y} + \frac{y^2}{\sigma_y^2}\right)\right\}$$

This is the normal bivariate probability function, or the normal correlation function.

Show further that any plane section of the surface $z = \phi(x,y)$ through the z-axis is a normal curve.

CHAPTER 10

Simple analysis of variance

10.1. In a certain examination, the papers written by students with different specialist subjects were awarded grades 1, 2, 3, 4 or 5 by different examiners; the question arose whether the examiners' standards were comparable. The distributions of grades awarded by five examiners gave the following statistics:

Subject	No. of candidates	Mean	Variance
History	64	3·18	1·208
Mathematics	28	3·29	0·926
Modern languages	50	3·22	1·292
Geography	35	3·43	1·045
Science	41	3·08	1·074
All candidates	218	3·22	1·151

The question we want to decide is whether the variation between the means is more than we should expect from random samples of the sizes indicated drawn from the same population; the technique of analysis of variance being introduced in this chapter provides a very suitable method of approach because we can deal with all the subjects simultaneously. The analysis of variance was developed by Fisher in the early 1920s.

Estimates of variance

10.2. The principle behind the analysis of variance is that two (or more) independent estimates are made of the variance of a population.

Suppose that k samples are taken from a population whose mean is μ. Let the ith sample have size n_i, mean m_i and let the combination of all the samples together have size n, mean m. We use $\sum_s, \sum$ to denote a summation over the k samples and n values of the variate respectively. We shall show that we can make two estimates of the variance of the population as follows:

$$\frac{\sum_s n_i(m_i-m)^2}{k-1}, \qquad \frac{\sum f(x-m_i)^2}{n-k}$$

Let us see how these arise.

In §7.6 we saw that the best estimate of σ^2, the variance of the population, we could make from a single sample was

$$\hat{\sigma}^2 = \frac{\sum f(x-m)^2}{n-1} \tag{28}$$

Now suppose that we knew only the means $m_1, m_2, \ldots, m_k$ of the k samples, what would be our best estimate of σ^2? For samples of size n_i, the variance of the mean is σ^2/n_i from **(19)**, i.e.

the mean value of $(m_i - \mu)^2$ is σ^2/n_i,

and so   the mean value of $n_i(m_i \doteq \mu)^2$ is σ^2.

If now we consider all k samples, we may take

$$\frac{\sum_s n_i(m_i - \mu)^2}{k} \tag{i}$$

as our estimate of σ^2. In fact we do not know the value of μ, the mean of the population, and so we have to use deviations from m instead and write the numerator of (i) as $\sum_s n_i(m_i - m)^2$. To compensate for this we divide by $k-1$ instead of k for the same reasons as were given in §7.6. Hence

$$\frac{\sum_s n_i(m_i - m)^2}{k-1} \tag{33}$$

gives an estimate for σ^2. Note that the k means have one linear constraint on them due to the mean m, leaving $k-1$ degrees of freedom, and that the denominator of **(33)** is $k-1$.

Referring back to the table at the beginning of the chapter, we find that

$$(k-1)\sigma^2 = 64(3{\cdot}18 - 3{\cdot}22)^2 + 28(3{\cdot}29 - 3{\cdot}22)^2 + 50(3{\cdot}22 - 3{\cdot}22)^2$$
$$+ 35(3{\cdot}43 - 3{\cdot}22)^2 + 41(3{\cdot}08 - 3{\cdot}22)^2$$

$$= 2{\cdot}5867$$

We have 5 samples, so $k-1=4$, and hence our estimate is

$$\sigma^2 = 0{\cdot}6467$$

We now turn to consider the expression

$$\frac{\sum f(x-m_i)^2}{n-k}$$

(Here the summation covers all n values of the variate but the deviations for the values of x in each sample are from the mean of that sample.) Let

$\sum^i$ denote a summation over the ith sample. If we take μ as an arbitrary origin, we have by **(7)** and **(8)**

$$\frac{\sum^i f(x-m_i)^2}{n_i} = \frac{\sum^i f(x-\mu)^2}{n_i} - (m_i-\mu)^2$$

$$\therefore \sum^i f(x-m_i)^2 = \sum^i f(x-\mu)^2 - n_i(m_i-\mu)^2$$

Summing over the k samples,

$$\sum f(x-m_i)^2 = \sum f(x-\mu)^2 - \sum_s n_i(m_i-\mu)^2$$

If we knew the value of μ, the best estimate we could make of σ^2 would be obtained by combining the samples and using **(7)**, giving

$$\frac{\sum f(x-\mu)^2}{n} \simeq \sigma^2$$

and by (i)

$$\frac{\sum_s n_i(m_i-\mu)^2}{k}$$

may be taken as an estimate of σ^2

$$\therefore \sum f(x-m_i)^2 \simeq n\sigma^2 - k\sigma^2$$

Therefore

$$\sum f(x-m_i)^2 \simeq (n-k)\sigma^2$$

So
$$\frac{\sum f(x-m_i)^2}{n-k} \tag{34}$$

(the deviations in each sample being taken from the mean of that sample) provides a second estimate of σ^2.

Note that the n values of x have k linear constraints on them due to the means of the k samples, leaving $n-k$ degrees of freedom, and that the denominator of **(34)** is also $n-k$.

This expression may easily be evaluated for the data given at the beginning of the chapter. If s_i^2 denotes the variance of the ith sample,

$$\sum^i f(x-m_i)^2 = n_i s_i^2*$$

---

* Sometimes the variance is calculated as

$$\frac{\sum^i f(x-m_i)^2}{n_i-1} \tag{28}$$

where possible, it should be discovered which formula is used.

Hence

$$\Sigma f(x-m_i)^2 = 64 \times 1\cdot208 + 28 \times 0\cdot926 + 50 \times 1\cdot292$$
$$+ 35 \times 1\cdot045 + 41 \times 1\cdot074$$
$$= 248\cdot45$$

But $n=218$ and $k=5$, so the variance 'within the samples'*

$$\frac{\Sigma f(x-m_i)^2}{n-k} = \frac{248\cdot45}{213} = 1\cdot166$$

Comparing this with the variance 'between the samples'*

$$\frac{\Sigma n_i(m_i-m)^2}{k-1} = 0\cdot6467$$

we see that the variance estimated from the means of the samples is *less* than the other estimate, i.e. the means show *less* variability than we should expect from five such random samples. This means that the data at the beginning of the chapter give us no reason to suppose that the standards of the examiners are different. (We cannot say that their standards are the same because we do not know that the quality of the candidates in the different subjects is the same.) Some readers may wonder why we do not use

$$\frac{\Sigma f(x-m)^2}{n-1}$$

as an estimate of σ^2. The answer is that **(33)** and **(34)** may be shown to be independent estimates—a requirement laid down by the test of significance to be described in §10.3—but the above is not independent of **(33)**.

Exercise 10a

1. T. Prove that, with the notation of §10.2,

$$\Sigma f(x-m)^2 = \Sigma f(x-m_i)^2 + \Sigma_s n_i(m_i-m)^2 \tag{35}$$

(Replace $x-m$ by $\{(x-m_i)+(m_i-m)\}$ in the left-hand side.)

Find the value of $\Sigma f(x-m)^2$ for the data of p. 157 and thus check the values of the numerators of **(33)** and **(34)** evaluated in the text.

2. Use the result of No. 1 to show that

$$\eta^2_{yx} = \frac{s^2_{m_y}}{s^2_y}$$

where $s^2_{m_y}$ is the weighted variance of the means of y for given x, i.e. $\frac{1}{n} \sum n_x(m_{y_x} - m_y)^2$. For the definition of η^2_{yx} see Exercise 9d, No. 2.

* These expressions are explained on p. 162.

Variance ratio

10.3. Having obtained two independent estimates of the variance of a population, it is necessary to have some test of significance which may be applied to them. This is provided (no proof will be given) by the ratio

$$F = \frac{s_1^2}{s_2^2} \qquad (s_1 > s_2)$$

where s_1^2, s_2^2 are two estimates of the variance, of which s_1 is the *greater*. This is tabulated in terms of v_1, v_2 the degrees of freedom of s_1, s_2; values of F for different levels of significance are found in Table D at the end of the book. This is a one-tailed test, giving the probability that the given value of F should be exceeded when two random samples are taken from the same population.

Fisher used another statistic $z = \frac{1}{2}\log_e F$ to test the significance of the ratio of variances and gave the distribution of z in 1924. Percentage points of F were given in 1934 by Snedecor, who chose F to denote the variance ratio in honour of Fisher.

Example 1. *The variance of the head-and-body lengths of 33 voles from Raasay (off Skye) was found to be 29·09 mm² while that for 40 voles from Reigate was found to be 56·39 mm². Can the difference between the variances be accounted for by sampling fluctuations?* (Calculated from Steven's data, L. Harrison Matthews, *British mammals*, 154.)

With the notation above,

$$s_1^2 = 56\cdot39, \qquad v_1 = 39$$

$$s_2^2 = 29\cdot09, \qquad v_2 = 32$$

$$F = \frac{s_1^2}{s_2^2} = \frac{56\cdot39}{29\cdot09} = 1\cdot938$$

Referring to Table D at the 5 per cent level, the critical value of F for $v_1 = 39$, $v_2 = 32$, lies between that for $v_1 = 24$, $v_2 = 30$, namely 1·89, and that for $v_1 = \infty$, $v_2 = 40$, namely 1·51. Hence the result is significant at the 5 per cent level. This evidence is by no means decisive but it is suggestive that the Reigate voles may show greater variability in head-and-body length than the Raasay voles.

Note. (1) The variances in Example 1 were calculated by **(28)**

$$\hat{\sigma}^2 = \frac{\sum f(x-m)^2}{n-1}$$

Had they been calculated as

$$\frac{\sum f(x-m)^2}{n}$$

we should have had to multiply them by a factor $n/(n-1)$.

(2) The n values of x are subject to one linear constraint imposed by the mean, and so have $n-1$ degrees of freedom.

Exercise 10b

1. Test the following pairs of variances (needed later on) for significance at the 5 per cent level:

(i) $s_1^2 = 10 \cdot 5$, $v_1 = 4$; $s_2^2 = 3 \cdot 75$, $v_2 = 8$.

(ii) $s_1^2 = 20$, $v_1 = 2$; $s_2^2 = 3 \cdot 75$, $v_2 = 8$.

2. Do the data of Exercise 7d, No. 1 (p. 125) provide evidence of greater variability among the lengths of German words than the English words from which they are translated? (Better still, make similar observations for yourself and test the results.)

3. Are the data of Exercise 7d, No. 2 (p. 125) consistent with the hypothesis that the distributions of draws in the Second and Fourth Divisions may be regarded as random samples from the same population?

Simple analysis of variance

10.4. We saw in §10.2 that two independent estimates of σ^2 are given by

$$\frac{\sum_s n_i(m_i-m)^2}{k-1} \quad (33), \qquad \frac{\sum f(x-m_i)^2}{n-k} \quad (34)$$

then in Exercise 10a, No. 1 the reader was asked to show that

$$\sum f(x-m)^2 = \sum f(x-m_i)^2 + \sum_s n_i(m_i-m)^2 \qquad (35)$$

This last result indicates that the sum of squares $\sum f(x-m)^2$ may be broken down into two parts. The first of these may be described as the contribution to the sum of squares from *within the samples* since the deviations are taken from the means of the samples. The second part of $\sum f(x-m)^2$ may be described as the contribution to the sum of squares from the variation *between the samples*, accordingly the two estimates for σ^2 given by

$$\frac{\sum_s n_i(m_i-m)^2}{k-1}, \qquad \frac{\sum f(x-m_i)^2}{n-k}$$

are referred to as the variance *between samples* and *within samples* respectively. The usual situation in which an analysis of variance is carried out is that there is thought to be more variation from one sample to another than is likely if they were random samples from the same population. If this is so, it will be reflected by a greater variance between samples than within samples.

It is useful to tabulate the sums of squares and degrees of freedom as follows:

	Sum of squares	Degrees of freedom	Estimate of σ^2
Between samples	$\sum_s n_i(m_i-m)^2$	$k-1$	$\dfrac{\sum_s n_i(m_i-m)^2}{k-1}$
Within samples	$\sum f(x-m_i)^2$	$n-k$	$\dfrac{\sum f(x-m_i)^2}{n-k}$
Total	$\sum f(x-m)^2$	$n-1$	—

Two checks are available since the third entry under 'sum of squares' and under 'degrees of freedom' is the sum of the other two. Alternatively, the sum of squares within samples, or between samples, may be found from the other two to save what may be considerable labour.

Example 2. *At a certain stage of the 1965–66 football season, the frequency distributions of the number of draws in the four divisions were as follows:*

| Division | \multicolumn{12}{c}{No. of draws} | Total |

Division	1	2	3	4	5	6	7	8	9	10	11	12	Total
First		1	5	4	4	3	3	2					22
Second	1	1	1	1	9		3	3			2	1	22
Third		2	2	5	4	2	6	2		1			24
Fourth	1		4	3	9	5		2					24
All	2	2	8	14	18	20	9	10	5	1	2	1	92

can the differences between the mean number of draws in the four divisions be attributed to random sampling?

We compute for the analysis of variance (i) the total sum of squares $\sum f(x-m)^2$, (ii) the sum of squares within divisions $\sum f(x-m_i)^2$.

For any sample, or for the whole distribution, we have from **(7)** and **(8)**

$$\sum f(x-m)^2 = \sum f(x-x_0)^2 - n(m-x_0)^2$$

163

Working has been carried out with $x_0 = 0$ on a machine; (for those without access to one, it would be better to take $x_0 = 5$, say.) The numbers in each row of the table below are obtained from the corresponding row of the table above.

Division	n	$\sum fx$	$\sum fx^2$	$nm^2 = (\sum fx)^2/n$	$\sum f(x-m)^2$
First	22	130	834	768·18	65·82
Second	22	152	1196	1050·18	145·82
Third	24	130	800	704·17	95·83
Fourth	24	116	618	560·67	57·33
All	92	528	3448	3030·26	417·74

The total sum of squares $\sum f(x-m)^2 = 417\cdot74$.

The sum of squares within divisions

$$\sum f(x-m_i)^2 = 65\cdot82 + 145\cdot82 + 95\cdot83 + 57\cdot33 = 364\cdot80.$$

Now by (35), the sum of squares between divisions*

$$\sum n_i(m_i - m)^2 = \sum f(x-m)^2 - \sum f(x-m_i)^2 = 417\cdot74 - 364\cdot80 = 52\cdot94.$$

The analysis of variance is therefore as follows:

	Sum of squares	Degrees of freedom	Estimate of σ^2
Between divisions	52·94	3	17·65
Within divisions	364·80	88	4·145
Total	417·74	91	—

Comparing the two estimates of the variance of the population,

$$F = \frac{17\cdot65}{4\cdot145} = 4\cdot26 \qquad (\nu_1 = 3, \nu_2 = 88)$$

For $\nu_1 = 3$, $\nu_2 = 60$, $F = 4\cdot13$ for significance at the 1 per cent level, so the result is significant at this level. Hence it would be unwise to conclude that the differences between the means are due to fluctuations in random sampling.

* Alternatively, though the labour is greater, $\sum n_i(m_i - m)^2$ may be evaluated from the means and (35) used as a check.

Exercise 10c

1. The following table gives data for scores on Valentine's Reasoning Tests for Higher Levels of Intelligence obtained by graduates. (C. W. Valentine, *British Journal of Educational Psychology*, 31 (iii).)

	1st class hons	2nd class hons	3rd class hons	Pass degree
Mean	50·00	42·48	35·63	31·64
No. of graduates	40	115	22	50
Standard deviation	14·08	13·92	13·85	15·16

Are the differences between the means significant? (Assume that the standard deviations are found from **(28)**.)

2. From a sample of 11-year-old Scottish school children, the I.Q.s of those born at different times of the year were found with the following results. (*The trend of Scottish intelligence*, Publication No. XXX of the Scottish Council for Research in Education, 1949.)

Month	I.Q.s of children of age 11			$\sum f(x-m_i)^2$	$n_i(m_i-m)^2$
	Number	Mean	S.D.		
Feb.	190	103·48	19·81	74 563	175·1
Apr.	227	104·48	21·45	104 443	872·0
June	222	103·88	20·72	95 309	410·6
Aug.	221	100·57	19·24	81 809	840·4
Oct.	178	101·97	20·02		
Dec.	177	100·25	18·25		

Complete the working started on the right and decide whether the differences between the means are significant. (It has been assumed that the standard deviations have been calculated from formula **(8)**; if $(n-1)$ was used as a divisor, the value of F will not be affected much.)

3. L. With the data of Exercise 10d, No. 4 (p. 174), apply an analysis of variance to the five sets of observations obtained at the meteorological stations concerned.

4. Samples were taken from a machine adjusted to dispense 750 g of detergent powder at a time; their frequency distributions were as follows.

Sample	Quantities in grams							Total
	747–	748–	749–	750–	751–	752–	753–	
A	1		4	3				8
B		1	3	3	1			8
C		1	2	4	1			8
D			2	3	2	1		8
E			1	3	2	1	1	8
F			3	3	2			8
G			2	4	1	1		8
H			1	2	4	1		8
Total	1	2	18	25	13	4	1	64

Would you say that the machine was dispensing powder steadily during the period covered by the samples?

5. The table below gives the number of children of parity 0, 1, 2, 3, 4 or more, born to mothers from different social classes during a certain survey. (The parity of a child is the number of children previously born to the mother. Butler and Bonham, *op. cit.*)

Social class	Parity					n	m	Σfx^2	$\Sigma f(x-m_i)^2$
	0	1	2	3	4 or more				
Professional, managerial	303	252	127	33	17	732	0·9194	1329	710·2
Intermediate (supervisory)	784	743	345	118	95	2085	1·0393	4705	2453·0
Skilled	3631	3032	1487	770	816	9736	1·1894	28966	15191·5
Partly skilled	622	550	335	175	272	1954	1·4498	7817	3709·9
Unskilled	440	449	271	172	244				
Others	504	189	86	58	72				
All groups	6284	5215	2651	1326	1516	16992	1·2099	52009	27134

Taking '4 or more' to be 4 in your working, investigate the hypothesis that the variation between the mean parity of children born to mothers in different social classes may be attributed to random sampling.

6. Show that, for two samples (in which the variance between means is greater than the variance within means) the value of F is the square of the value of t obtained by the method of §7.8, p. 124.

Three components: introduction

10.5. The full power of the method of analysis of variance was by no means apparent in the previous sections. The great advantage of it as a research tool is that it enables the investigator to vary more than one factor at a time. The following simple, artificial example has been chosen to illustrate this.

Suppose that a farmer wishes to compare the breeding qualities of a number of sows and to compare the merits of a number of different feeding methods simultaneously. (In some experiments three factors are varied simultaneously, but we shall consider the simpler case only.) He has three litters of the same age and he is anxious to compare five feeding methods employed when the piglets are being weaned, so he selects 15 piglets, as near the same weight as he can, 5 from each litter, and starts his experiment. We come in later on when he shows us the following table of weights gained in lb.

		Feeding methods					
		A	B	C	D	E	Mean
Litters	1	26	24	22	20	18	22
	2	21	21	20	20	18	20
	3	19	18	21	14	18	18
Mean		22	21	21	18	18	20

Looking back to §10.2, p. 157, for guidance as to a possible method of analysis, we see that

$$\frac{\sum_s n_i(m_i - m)^2}{k - 1} \tag{33}$$

can still be used although we shall need to modify the symbols used in order to avoid confusion between the means of the rows and the columns. Writing $_r m_i$ for the mean of the ith row and $_c m_j$ for the mean of the jth column, if there are h rows and k columns,

for *feeding methods* (treating columns as samples)

$$\frac{\sum_s h(_c m_j - m)^2}{k - 1}$$

$$= \frac{3(22-20)^2 + 3(21-20)^2 + 3(21-20)^2 + 3(18-20)^2 + 3(18-20)^2}{4}$$

$$= 10 \cdot 5$$

167

7

While for *litters* (treating rows as samples)

$$\frac{\sum_s k(_rm_i - m)^2}{h-1} = \frac{5(22-20)^2 + 5(20-20)^2 + 5(18-20)^2}{2} = 20$$

Here, then, we have two estimates of the variance of the population; but we shall need an independent estimate in order to determine whether the variation in the means of the rows, or the columns, may be ascribed to chance. In the earlier sections of this chapter we used

$$\frac{\sum f(x-m_i)^2}{n-k} \tag{34}$$

as an independent estimate of the variance of the population, but this formula is not directly applicable since there are *two* means corresponding to each gain in weight and there are no longer $n-k$ degrees of freedom. We must therefore look for some property which can be carried over into the new situation; this we find in

$$\sum f(x-m)^2 = \sum f(x-m_i)^2 + \sum_s n_i(m_i-m)^2 \tag{35}$$

(obtained in Exercise 10a, No. 1) which enables us to write the numerator of (34) as

$$\sum f(x-m)^2 - \sum_s n_i(m_i-m)^2$$

This suggests that for our present case (remembering that we have two sets of means and that $f=1$) we should examine the expression

$$\sum (x-m)^2 - \sum_c h(_cm_j-m)^2 - \sum_r k(_rm_i-m)^2 \tag{36}$$

$\sum_c, \sum_r$ denoting summations over the column and row means.

Considering first the columns, it follows from (35) that

$$\sum (x-m)^2 = \sum (x-_cm_j)^2 + \sum_c h(_cm_j-m)^2$$

so that on substitution, (36) becomes

$$\sum (x-_cm_j)^2 - \sum_r k(_rm_i-m)^2 \tag{i}$$

To simplify this expression, consider the contribution from row i, namely

$$\sum_{j=1}^{k} (x-_cm_j)^2 - k(_rm_i-m)^2$$

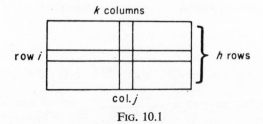

FIG. 10.1

Writing $z = x - {}_c m_j$, the mean value of z

$$\bar{z} = \frac{1}{k} \sum_j (x - {}_c m_j) \tag{4}$$

$$= \frac{1}{k} \sum_j x - \frac{1}{k} \sum_j {}_c m$$

$$= {}_r m_i - m$$

(the latter term is m because each mean is obtained from an equal number of values of x.) So the contribution to (i) from row i is

$$\sum_j z^2 - k\bar{z}^2$$

which by **(7)** and **(9)** may be written

$$\sum_j (z - \bar{z})^2$$

or, substituting for $z, \bar{z}$,

$$\sum_j (x - {}_c m_j - {}_r m_i + m)^2$$

Now, summing for all rows, it follows that **(36)** may be written

$$\Sigma \, (x - {}_c m_j - {}_r m_i + m)^2 \tag{36a}$$

This expression, for reasons we shall see later, is termed the *interaction* sum of squares.

Now let us see whether **(36a)**, or its equivalent form **(36)**, gives us an estimate of σ^2 the variance of the population.

$$\Sigma \, (x - m)^2 \simeq (hk - 1) \sigma^2 \qquad \text{by (28)}$$

$$\Sigma_c \, h({}_c m_j - m)^2 \simeq (k - 1) \sigma^2 \qquad \text{by (33)}$$

$$\Sigma_r \, k({}_r m_j - m)^2 \simeq (h - 1) \sigma^2 \qquad \text{by (33)}$$

so that **(36)** and **(36a)** are approximately equal to

$$\{(hk - 1) - (k - 1) - (h - 1)\} \sigma^2 = (hk - h - k + 1) \sigma^2$$

$$= (h - 1)(k - 1) \sigma^2$$

So an estimate of σ^2 may be obtained by dividing either **(36)** or **(36a)** by $(h - 1)(k - 1)$.

Question 1. How many degrees of freedom has a frequency table of h rows and k columns, if the mean of each row and column is given?

169

Once again, we find that the sum of squares divided by the degrees of freedom gives an estimate of σ^2.

Three components: interaction

10.6. The numerical example with which we began the previous section will help to bring out the nature of the 'interaction' sum of squares,

$$\Sigma\,(x - {_c}m_j - {_r}m_i + m)^2 \tag{36a}$$

which may be rewritten

$$\Sigma\,\{(x - m) - ({_c}m_j - m) - ({_r}m_i - m)\}^2$$

The table of weights gained was

		Feeding methods					
		A	B	C	D	E	Mean
	1	26	24	22	20	18	22
Litters	2	21	21	20	20	18	20
	3	19	18	21	14	18	18
Mean		22	21	21	18	18	20

We can compensate for the differences between feeding methods by subtracting $({_c}m_j - m)$ from each entry in the body of the table, bringing all the column means to the same value 20:

		Feeding methods					
		A	B	C	D	E	Mean
	1	24	23	21	22	20	22
Litters	2	19	20	19	22	20	20
	3	17	17	20	16	20	18
Mean		20	20	20	20	20	20

We can now compensate for the difference between litters by subtracting $({_r}m_i - m)$ from each entry, thus bringing all the row means to the same value 20:

| | Feeding methods | | | | | |
	A	B	C	D	E	Mean
1	22	21	19	20	18	20
Litters 2	19	20	19	22	20	20
3	19	19	22	18	22	20
Mean	20	20	20	20	20	20

Then the interaction sum of squares is the sum of the squares of the deviations of these adjusted weights from 20—it is not difficult to show that their sum is 30. *Note.* In practice, the simplest way to obtain the interaction sum of squares is by **(36)**. See also Question 2.

Since we have allowed for differences between the feeding methods and between the litters, to what should we attribute the remaining deviations from 20?

(1) Even if all the piglets had the same heredity and the same feeding, we should not expect their gains in weight to be exactly equal—such variation we might ascribe to *chance*.

(2) In practice there will be real differences between the piglets—some will use up more energy by running than others, some will have bigger appetites, and so on—so there may be *real differences* from one piglet to another for which we have not allowed. (Possible error from this source should be guarded against by assigning the piglets at random to the different feeding methods.)

(3) It is possible that a particular feeding method suits one litter better than another. This may not seem likely in the present case but if, instead of piglets, we were considering cows yielding different quantities of milk, we should certainly expect the diet to affect, or *interact* with, the output of milk. Thus the factors being investigated may not be independent of each other and some of the variation may, in certain cases, be attributed to *interaction* between these factors.

In a slightly more complicated analysis of variance, the existence of interaction between the factors being investigated may be detected by examining the magnitude of the variance estimated from the interaction sum of squares (called the *interaction variance*) and comparing it with yet another estimate of the variance. Here, however, the interaction variance takes the place of the 'within samples' variance of §10.4 and is used in the same way. When it is used in this manner, it is often called the *residual* variance being, as we saw in the last paragraph, the variance calculated from the sum of squares 'left over' when we have compensated for differences between the means of the rows and columns.

Three components: analysis of variance

10.7. The analysis of variance may be presented as follows:

	Sum of squares	Degrees of freedom	Estimate of σ^2
Columns	$\sum_c h(_c m_j - m)^2$	$k-1$	$\dfrac{\sum_c h(_c m_j - m)^2}{k-1}$
Rows	$\sum_r k(_r m_i - m)^2$	$h-1$	$\dfrac{\sum_r k(_r m_i - m)^2}{h-1}$
Interaction or residual	$\sum (x - _c m_j - _r m_i + m)^2$	$(h-1)(k-1)$	$\dfrac{\sum (x - _c m_j - _r m_i + m)^2}{(h-1)(k-1)}$
Total	$\sum (x-m)^2$	$hk-1$	—

For the example introduced in §10.5 we have:

	Sum of squares	Degrees of freedom	Estimate of σ^2
Feeding methods	42	4	10·5
Litters	40	2	20
Residual	30	8	3·75
Total	112	14	—

Question 2. Check the value of the residual sum of squares from the last table of §10.6, p. 171.

Also check the total sum of squares from the first table of §10.5, p. 167.

Check that the total degrees of freedom is both $(nk-1)$ and the sum of the other degrees of freedom.

We can now use the variance ratio of §10.3, p. 161, to test the hypothesis that the estimates of the variance have been obtained with random samples from the same population:

for *feeding methods*

$$F = \frac{10 \cdot 5}{3 \cdot 75} = 2 \cdot 67, \qquad \nu_1 = 4, \nu_2 = 8$$

with these degrees of freedom, $F = 3.84$ for significance at the 5 per cent level (Table D), so this result is not significant;

for *litters*

$$F = \frac{20}{3.75} = 5.33, \qquad \nu_1 = 2, \nu_2 = 8$$

with these degrees of freedom, $F = 4.46$ for significance at the 5 per cent level and $F = 8.65$ for significance at the 1 per cent level, so this result is significant at the 5 per cent level.

We may conclude, then, that there is no evidence that any particular one of the feeding methods employed is superior to the others; on the other hand, the differences between the litters may well be caused by factors other than sampling fluctuations. The 5 per cent level of significance is, of course, completely arbitrary and this example, in which one test comes out as significant and the other not, underlines its arbitrary nature. It may be that there are advantages in one feeding method which are quite small and so have not shown up in the experiment, on the other hand it may be that the differences between the litters has been thrown up by chance. Still, as a guide to action, the results suggest that it might be better to breed from Litter 1 rather than the others, and that the choice of feeding method should be dictated by convenience—assuming, as we have done for the sake of simplicity, that the costs are equal.

Exercise 10d

1. L. If the origin and unit of measurement are changed throughout, will there be any difference made to the values of F obtained in an analysis of variance?

2. Five varieties of pea plant were treated with different fertilisers and the weight of peas obtained from 25 experimental plots were as follows.

		Fertilisers				
		1	2	3	4	5
Varieties of pea	A	43	38	35	38	36
	B	46	33	40	39	27
	C	40	38	40	40	32
	D	35	41	29	36	34
	E	41	35	31	42	36

Are the differences between varieties or fertilisers significant? (Take a working origin as suggested in No. 1.)

3. Three sides of an 'equilateral' triangle were measured in inches by 5 people with the following results.

		Pupils				
		A	B	C	D	E
Sides	a	5·44	5·41	5·43	5·42	5·43
	b	5·43	5·41	5·42	5·43	5·44
	c	5·45	5·42	5·43	5·43	5·44

Are there any significant differences between (i) the pupils, (ii) the sides of the triangle? (Use the result of No. 1.)

4. The numbers of Rain-days (0·01 in or more) for the months of 1960 are given for five meteorological stations (Meteorological Office, *British rainfall 1959–1960*, H.M.S.O.).

Station	Jan.	Feb.	Mar.	Apr.	May	June	Jul.	Aug.	Sep.	Oct.	Nov.	Dec.	Sum	Sum of squares
Dover	23	15	11	10	8	10	18	19	12	24	23	24	197	3649
Southampton	17	17	16	15	11	11	22	21	17	22	26	22	217	4159
Farnborough	19	18	14	14	10	13	19	17	14	27	26	18	209	3921
Oxford	25	13	14	12	9	15	21	15	12	25	26	22	209	4035
Cambridge	19	13	7	7	5	12	19	15	13	22	22	20	174	2920
Sum	103	76	62	58	43	61	99	87	68	120	123	106	1006	18684
Sum of squares	2165	1176	818	714	391	759	1971	1541	942	2898	3041	2268	18684	

Can the differences between the stations be accounted for by fluctuations of random sampling?

5. The number of chairs produced by a factory in the 40 working hours of a certain week are given in the table below.

	Hour of working day							
	1	2	3	4	5	6	7	8
Monday	84	91	87	94	89	84	91	92
Tuesday	96	97	96	93	96	93	90	83
Wednesday	88	91	91	94	99	92	98	99
Thursday	87	96	94	95	87	91	90	88
Friday	95	85	97	84	84	95	81	83

Are the variations from one hour to another and from one day to another significant?

Answers

Chapter 1

Exercise 1b (*page* 3)

1. $\frac{3}{13}$.
2. False: some letters are used more frequently than others.
3. All $\frac{1}{10}$. No.
4. $\frac{1}{36}, \frac{2}{36}, \frac{3}{36}, \frac{4}{36}, \frac{5}{36}, \frac{6}{36}, \frac{5}{36}, \frac{4}{36}, \frac{3}{36}, \frac{2}{36}, \frac{1}{36}$; 1.
5. $\frac{1}{4}$.

Exercise 1c (*page* 4)

1. $\frac{1}{4}, \frac{3}{4}$.
2. $\frac{215}{216}, \frac{212}{216}$.
3. $8, \frac{7}{8}$.

Exercise 1d (*page* 4)

1. (iv), (vi).

Exercise 1e (*page* 5)

2. (i) $\frac{3}{10}$, (ii) $\frac{1}{10}$, (iii) $\frac{4}{10}$.
3. (i) $\frac{1}{2}$, (ii) $\frac{1}{5}$. The events are not mutually exclusive.
4. 16, (i) $\frac{1}{16}$, (ii) $\frac{1}{8}$.
5. (i) $\frac{1}{216}$, (ii) $\frac{5}{72}$, (iii) $\frac{2}{27}$.
6. If m mutually exclusive events have probabilities $p_1, p_2, \ldots, p_m$, the probability that one of them should occur is $p_1 + p_2 + \ldots + p_m$.

Exercise 1f (*page* 7)

1. Replace the card and shuffle well.
2. Yes.
3. No: he is likely to improve with practice.

Question 3 (*page* 8). If m independent events have probabilities $p_1, p_2, \ldots, p_m$, the probability that all of them should occur is $p_1 p_2 \ldots p_m$.

Exercise 1g (*page* 8)

1. (i) $\frac{1}{169}$, (ii) $\frac{1}{16}$.
2. (i) $\frac{25}{676}$, (ii) $\frac{9}{169}$, (iii) $\frac{15}{338}$.
3. (i) $\frac{1}{64}$, (ii) $\frac{9}{64}$, (iii) $\frac{27}{64}$.
4. $\frac{5}{8}$.
5. $1 - \left(\frac{19}{20}\right)^6 \simeq 0 \cdot 26$.

Statistics

Exercise 1h (*page* 9)

1. (i) $\frac{1}{6}$, (ii) $\frac{5}{18}$.
3. 0·504.

2. (i) $\frac{1}{30}$, (ii) $\frac{1}{6}$.

Exercise 1i (*page* 10)

2. $\frac{1}{9}, \frac{4}{9}, \frac{4}{9}$.
4. Yes: $(\frac{1}{3}+\frac{2}{3})^2$, $(\frac{1}{2}+\frac{1}{2})^4$.
6. 3:4.

3. 6; $\frac{1}{16}, \frac{1}{4}, \frac{3}{8}, \frac{1}{4}, \frac{1}{16}$.
5. $q^3, 3q^2 p, 3qp^2, p^3$.
7. $\frac{19}{20}$.

8. 46. *Hint.* $(\frac{19}{20})^n < \frac{1}{10}$. Solve $(\frac{20}{19})^n = 10$ by taking logs of both sides.
9. 17.
10. A: $\frac{1}{6}+(\frac{5}{6})^2(\frac{1}{6})+\ldots=\frac{1}{6}\times$ (sum of G.P. to infinity) $=\frac{6}{11}$.
  B: $(\frac{5}{6})(\frac{1}{6})+(\frac{5}{6})^3(\frac{1}{6})+\ldots=\frac{5}{11}$.
11. $\frac{81}{400}, \frac{3}{11}, \frac{6}{11}$.

12. 1225:1296:1260.

Chapter 2

Exercise 2a (*page* 13)

2. $179\frac{5}{9}$ lb, 128 lb.

3. (i) $\sum x^2$, (ii) $\sum \frac{x-a}{n} = \frac{1}{n}\sum (x-a)$.

4. (i) $(x_1-a)^2+(x_2-a)^2+\ldots+(x_n-a)^2$,

  (ii) $\frac{x_1^2-a^2}{n}+\frac{x_2^2-a^2}{n}+\ldots+\frac{x_n^2-a^2}{n}=\frac{1}{n}(x_1^2+x_2^2+\ldots+x_n^2)-a^2$.

Exercise 2b (*page* 14)

2. 5 ft 9·7 in.

3. 35·33 ft.

Exercise 2c (*page* 18)

2. 4·613.

3. 1·813.

Exercise 2d (*page* 21)

3. 4·732.

4. $1\frac{1}{3}$.

Exercise 2e (*page* 24)

1. (i) 70·5 in., (ii) 7·8 sec.
3. 16 yr 5·1 mo.
5. 19·17 cm.
7. 21·50 oz.
9. 69·53 in.
11. $\sum f(x_0'-x_0)=n(x_0'-x_0)$.

4. 9·96 lb.
6. 56 300.
8. 34·39 ton/h.
10. 18 453.

12. Males 13·28 yr, females 14·05 yr, difference 0·77 yr.

13. (i) 24·984, (ii) 25·125; difference 0·141.

Mid-value	2	7	12	17	22	27	32	37	42	47	52	57
Frequency	3	3	8	13	8	10	4	3	5	2	2	3

Chapter 3

Question 1 (*page* 32). $\sqrt{4\cdot8} \simeq 2\cdot19$ in.

Exercise 3a (*page* 33)

1. Taking the ages to be given exactly, $m = 10$ apples; estimating the ages to be $4\frac{1}{2}$, $6\frac{1}{2}$, etc., $m = 10\frac{1}{2}$ apples; in either case $s = 4\cdot04$ apples.

2. 71 per cent, 93 per cent, 100 per cent.

3. $\sqrt{1\frac{1}{2}} = 1\cdot225$

4. $\sqrt{6\frac{2}{3}} = 2\cdot58$. No change in answer.

5. (i) $1\frac{3}{4}$, (ii) $\frac{3}{4}$, (iii) $1\frac{3}{4}$; $\frac{3}{4}$.

6. Yes.

7. They are equal.

8. $s^2 = \dfrac{1}{n} \sum f(x-x_0)^2 - (m-x_0)^2.$

Exercise 3b (*page* 37)

2. 1·51.

3. $\sqrt{\frac{8}{9}} = 0\cdot943$.

4. 63 per cent, 98 per cent, 100 per cent; 69 per cent, 98 per cent, 100 per cent.

Exercise 3c (*page* 39)

1. $m = 16$ yr 5·3 mo, $s = 5\cdot94$ mo.

2. Exercise 2e, No. 4: 1·56 lb;

  No. 5: 3·16 cm;

  No. 6: 9050;

  No. 7: 1·48 oz;

  No. 8: 0·821(5) ton/h;

  No. 9: 2·56 in.

3. $n\{(m-x_0)^2 - (m-x_0')^2\}$.

4. The standard deviation would be unaltered.

5. 13·91 from original marks, 13·93 from grouped. Difference 0·02.

7. $\sum f + \sum f\left(\dfrac{x-x_0}{c}\right) = \sum f\left(\dfrac{x-x_0}{c}+1\right).$

Chapter 4

Exercise 4a (*page* 42)

1. (ii), (iv) nearly so.

Exercise 4b (*page* 44)

1. 1.

2.

No. of heads	0	1	2	3	4	5	6
P	$\dfrac{1}{2^6}$	$\dfrac{6}{2^6}$	$\dfrac{15}{2^6}$	$\dfrac{20}{2^6}$	$\dfrac{15}{2^6}$	$\dfrac{6}{2^6}$	$\dfrac{1}{2^6}$

3.

No. of heads	0	1	2	3	4	5	6	7	8
P	$\dfrac{1}{2^8}$	$\dfrac{8}{2^8}$	$\dfrac{28}{2^8}$	$\dfrac{56}{2^8}$	$\dfrac{70}{2^8}$	$\dfrac{56}{2^8}$	$\dfrac{28}{2^8}$	$\dfrac{8}{2^8}$	$\dfrac{1}{2^8}$

4.

No. of heads	0	1	...	r	...	n
P	$\dfrac{1}{2^n}$	$\dfrac{n}{2^n}$	...	$\dfrac{n!}{(n-r)!\,r!}\dfrac{1}{2^n}$	...	$\dfrac{1}{2^n}$

5. (i) $\frac{105}{512}$, (ii) $\frac{63}{256}$, (iii) $\frac{105}{512}$.

Exercise 4c (*page* 46)

1.

No. of sixes	0	1	2	3
Theoretical frequency	125	75	15	1

2. 0·080.

3. 0·9, 10·9, 48·8, 80·1, 48·8, 10·9, 0·9.

4. (i) 0·86, (ii) 0·14.

5. 53/3125 = 0·017.

6. (i) $1·81 \times 10^{-18}$, (ii) 0·39.

7. 0·24.

8.

No. of successes	0	1	2	3	4	5	6	7	8	9	10
$100\,P$	2·8	12·1	23·3	26·7	20·0	10·3	3·7	0·9	0·1	0·0	0·0

9. $1\frac{1}{3}$.

Exercise 4d (*page* 48)

1. 1·2.

3. $\mu = x_0 + \sum P(x - x_0)$.

5. (i) p, (ii) $2p$, (iii) $3p$; $4p$.

7. 6.

8.

9. (iii) μ.

Length of run	1	2	...	n	...
P	$\frac{1}{2}$	$\frac{1}{4}$	...	$\frac{1}{2^n}$	...

$\mu = 2$, $\sigma = \sqrt{2}$.

Exercise 4e (*page* 51)

1. $\sqrt{1\frac{1}{2}} = 1\cdot225$.

2. $\frac{1}{6}\sqrt{15} = 0\cdot6455$.

3. (i) $\sqrt{(pq)}$, (ii) $\sqrt{(2pq)}$, (iii) $\sqrt{(3pq)}$; $\sqrt{(4pq)}$.

5. $\sigma^2 = \sum P(x - x_0)^2 - (\mu - x_0)^2$.

6. $\sqrt{30} = 5\cdot477$. (*Hint*: See answer to Exercise 1i, No. 10.)

7. $\sqrt{\mu}$.

8. $\sqrt{\dfrac{n^2 - 1}{12}}$.

Exercise 4f (*page* 55)

1. See No. 2.

4. $\left(0, \dfrac{1}{\sqrt{(2\pi)}}\right), \left(\pm 1, \dfrac{1}{\sqrt{(2\pi e)}}\right)$.

Question 3 (*page* 56). (i) 0·00621, (ii) 0·1498, (iii) 0·9332, (iv) 0·3830, (v) 0·7745.

Exercise 4g (*page* 57)

2. 1.

3. 0, $a/\sqrt{3}$. $\phi(x) = \dfrac{1}{\sigma\sqrt{(2\pi)}}\, e^{-\frac{1}{2}(x-\mu)^2/\sigma}$

Exercise 4h (*page* 60)

1. (i) 0·0062, (ii) 0·0425. **2.** 0·1469.

3. 0·9999.

Exercise 4i (*page* 61)

1. (i) 0·0228, (ii) 0·0684; 112·6.

2. (i) 22·8 to 23·8 ft, (ii) 21·9 to 24·7 ft.

3. (i) 67·78 to 71·22 in., (ii) 0·163.

4. $67\frac{5}{8}$ in., 3·57 in. (90 per cent may be very rough.)

5. (i) $\pm 1\cdot51$, (ii) $\pm 4\cdot39$.

Exercise 4j (*page* 66)

1.

No. of peas	0	1	2	3	4	5	6	7	8	9	Total
Frequency	0·4	2·1	8·2	21·0	35·5	39·2	28·3	13·4	4·1	1·0	153·2

2.

Rate	31·75	32·15	32·55	32·95	33·35	33·75	34·15	34·55
Frequency	0·4	1·1	3·5	8·8	17·8	28·4	36·3	37·0

	34·95	35·35	35·75	36·15	36·55	36·95	Total
	30·3	19·8	10·3	4·3	1·4	0·5	199·9

4.

x	$z = \dfrac{x - m}{s}$	P	nP	Frequency
			298·5	
				258·1
500	0·1496	0·5594	556·6	
				234·3
600	0·8235	0·7949	790·9	
				137·3
700	1·497	0·9328	928·1	
				52·0
800	2·171	0·9850	980·1	
				12·7

5.

$m = 6·482, s = 1·577.$

Belt no.	0	1	2	3	4	5	6
Frequency	0·1	0·7	5·0	23·5	75·0	162·3	237·8

	7	8	9	10	11	12	Total
	236·5	158·8	72·5	22·4	4·7	0·7	1000·0

7. (i) 0·3413(5), (ii) 0·00136.

Chapter 5

Exercise 5a (*page* 71)

1. S.D. of distribution in Fig. 5.1 is 9·3, that of cards 28·87.

Exercise 5b (*page* 76)

1. Both highly significant, deviations $7.65\sigma_p$, $8.39\sigma_p$.
2. Not significant, deviation $1.2\sigma_p$.
3. Deviation $< \sigma_p$; not significant.

Exercise 5c (*page* 80)

1. Consider the hypothesis that the probability of B being right for any card is $\frac{1}{2}$. Deviation $1.94\sigma_p$. Not significant at 5 per cent level.
2. Deviation $1.90\sigma_p$. Not significant at 5 per cent level.
3. Deviation $1.14\sigma_p$; not significant.
4. No. Deviation $14.4\sigma_p$. Very highly significant.
5. From 40 to 60 and from 37 to 63.
6. (i) Between 37.8 per cent and 42.2 per cent, (ii) between 37.1 per cent and 42.9 per cent.

7. $\dfrac{98^2}{x^2}$

Exercise 5d (*page* 85)

1. $\sigma_x \propto 1/\sqrt{n}$.
2. Experimental value 9.3 agrees well with theoretical value 9.129.
3. (i) 1.708, (ii) 2.415; 1.208.

Exercise 5e (*page* 88)

2. Deviation $2.36\sigma_m$. Significant at 2 per cent level.
3. Deviation $2\sigma_m$. $P = 0.046$.
4. From 96.47 to 103.53.
5. $\mu = 6$, $\sigma = \sqrt{3}$; In formula $\sigma/\sqrt{n}$, we take $n = 4096$ because the sample consists of 4096 throws of a dozen dice. $\sigma_m = \sqrt{3}/\sqrt{4096}$. Deviation $4.6\sigma_m$. Very highly significant.

Chapter 6

Exercise 6a (*page* 94)

2. See p. 101, Exercise 6c, No. 5 for the bivariate frequency distribution.
3. 0.36.   **4.** 0.
6. There is a linear equation connecting x, y.

Exercise 6c (*page* 100)

1. 0.79.
3. 0.334 compared with 0.357 when computed without grouping. The slight reduction is due to grouping.

4. -0.17.   **5.** $\frac{1}{2}$.

6.

		Number of heads				
		0	1	2	3	4
No. of heads	0	1	4	6	4	1
	1	4	16	24	16	4
	2	6	24	36	24	6
	3	4	16	24	16	4
	4	1	4	6	4	1

Note: Each entry in the body of this table should be divided by 256.
Yes, the contribution of each row (and column) to $\sum P(x-\mu_x)(y-\mu_y)$ is zero.

7. 0.80.

Exercise 6d (*page* 104)

1. Taking $\zeta = 0$, $z/\sigma_z = -1.72$; not significant.

2.

		n		
		100	200	500
Level	5%	0.20	0.14	0.09
	1%	0.26	0.18	0.12
	0.1%	0.33	0.23	0.15

3. $0.65 < r < 0.84$; 0.017.

Chapter 7

Exercise 7a (*page* 106)

1. $\sigma_{x+y}^2 = \sigma_x^2 + \sigma_y^2 + 2\rho\sigma_x\sigma_y$.
2. Replace $(1/n) \sum f$ by $\sum P$.
3. (Each entry for P to be divided by 36.)

		x					
		1	2	3	4	5	6
	6	1	1	1	1	1	1
	5	1	1	1	1	1	1
y	4	1	1	1	1	1	1
	3	1	1	1	1	1	1
	2	1	1	1	1	1	1
	1	1	1	1	1	1	1

$x+y$	2	3	4	5	6	7	8	9	10	11	12
P	1	2	3	4	5	6	5	4	3	2	1

$x-y$	-5	-4	-3	-2	-1	0	1	2	3	4	5
P	1	2	3	4	5	6	5	4	3	2	1

$\sigma = \frac{1}{6}\sqrt{210} \simeq 2\cdot42$. Because x and y are uncorrelated.

4. $\sigma_1^2 + \sigma_2^2$; $\sigma_1^2 + \sigma_2^2 + \ldots + \sigma_n^2$.

5. $\phi(x) = 1$, $-\frac{1}{2} \leqslant x < \frac{1}{2}$; $1/\sqrt{12} \simeq 0\cdot2887$; 1, $1/\sqrt{12}$.

Exercise 7b (*page* 111)

1. Length: diff. $= 4\cdot95 \times$ s.e.; breadth: diff. $= 4\cdot8 \times$ s.e. Both very highly significant. No.

2. Diff. $= 0\cdot51 \times$ s.e. Not significant.

3. Diff. $= 0\cdot69 \times$ s.e. Not significant.

4. Diff. $= 4\cdot5 \times$ s.e. Very highly significant. No.

5. Diff. $= 6\cdot0 \times$ s.e. Very highly significant.

6. 16 400; between 14 400 and 18 400.

7. Diff. $= 4\cdot4 \times$ s.e. Very highly significant. No.

Exercise 7c (*page* 118)

1. Diff. $= 2\cdot5 \times$ s.e. Significant at 2 per cent level.

2. Diff. $= 3\cdot2 \times$ s.e. Significant at 1 per cent level. Diff. $= 5\cdot1 \times$ s.e. Very highly significant.

3. Social classes: Professional v. non-manual, diff. $= 4\cdot8 \times$ s.e., Non-manual v. skilled diff. $= 4\cdot6 \times$ s.e.

Residence: North v. Central, diff. $= 6\cdot9 \times$ s.e., Central v. South, diff. $= 3\cdot0 \times$ s.e.

All differences very highly significant, except the last, which is significant at 1 per cent level.

4. Diff. $= 0\cdot42 \times$ s.e. Not significant.

5.

		Proportion of pennies			
		0	$\frac{1}{4}$	$\frac{1}{2}$	$\frac{3}{4}$	1
Proportion of halfpennies	1	1	4	6	4	1
	$\frac{3}{4}$	4	16	24	16	4
	$\frac{1}{2}$	6	24	36	24	6
	$\frac{1}{4}$	4	16	24	16	4
	0	1	4	6	4	1

Entries in the body of the table to be divided by 256.

Difference between proportions	-1	$-\frac{3}{4}$	$-\frac{1}{2}$	$-\frac{1}{4}$	0	$\frac{1}{4}$	$\frac{1}{2}$	$\frac{3}{4}$	1
Probability $\times 256$	1	8	28	56	70	56	28	8	1

Probability of proportions r, s of heads in sets of heads and pennies and halfpennies $\binom{n}{r}\binom{n}{s}\left(\frac{1}{2}\right)^{2n}$.

Question 1. (*page* 123) $t = 2.26$, $\nu = 19$. Significant at the 5 per cent level. Suggestive but inconclusive.

Exercise 7d (*page* 125)

1. Diff. $= 1.5 \times$ s.e. Not significant. Such a difference could easily have arisen by chance.
2. Significant at the 1 per cent level.
3. Yes. Diff. $= 1.4 \times$ s.e. Not significant.
4. Diff. $= 7.9 \times$ s.e. Very highly significant.
5. $n_1 + n_2 - 2$.

Chapter 8

Question 1. (*page* 129). 4,3.

Exercise 8a (*page* 129)

1. 2.
2.

3. 4;

	A	B	C	D	E
T	400	500	300	200	100
M	800	1000	600	400	200
S	400	500	300	200	100

	A	B	C
E	9	10	11
I	18	20	22
D	27	30	33

5. 6.
6. $n - 1$.
7. $(k-1)(n-1)$, $k+n-1$; $k+n$ equations may be written down from the row and column totals but the sums of the row and column totals are equal so that only $k+n-1$ equations are independent.

Exercise 8b (*page* 135)

1. $\chi^2 = 3.04$, $\nu = 3$, $0.3 < P < 0.5$; consistent.
2. χ^2 would be doubled.
3. $\chi^2 = 6.4$, $\nu = 2$, $P < 0.05$. Doubt is thrown on the hypothesis.

4. $\chi^2 = 10\cdot7$ and $13\cdot5$, the former is a better fit but P is small ($0\cdot01 < P < 0\cdot02$).
5. $\chi^2 = 2\cdot9$, $\nu = 4$, $0\cdot5 < P < 0\cdot7$; no.
6. $\chi^2 = 0\cdot40$, $P < 0\cdot01$.
8. With variate χ^2, $y = \frac{1}{2}e^{-\frac{1}{2}\chi^2}$, $y = \frac{1}{4}\chi^2 e^{-\frac{1}{2}\chi^2}$.
9. $\chi^2 = 193$ (the difference is due to the fact that the units figure of the theoretical frequencies is only approximate.)
10. No. $P < 0\cdot01$.

Exercise 8c (*page* 140)

2.

$f-F$	$(f-F)^2$	$(f-F)^2/F$
11	121	0·599
−10	100	0·725
−10	100	2·128
9	81	6·231

Check: 0 $\qquad\qquad \chi^2 = 9\cdot683$, $\nu = 3$, $0\cdot02 < P < 0\cdot05$.

Agreement only moderately close.
3. 3 (from total, mean and standard deviation).
No. 1: with first three and last two cells together, $\chi^2 = 5\cdot63$; $\nu = 4$, $0\cdot2 < P < 0\cdot3$, satisfactory agreement.
No. 2: with first and last three cells together, $\chi^2 = 4\cdot71$, $\nu = 7$, $0\cdot5 < P < 0\cdot7$, good agreement.
4.

No. of males	0	1	2	3	4	5	6	7	8	Total
Theoretical frequency	1·6	12·6	44·0	87·9	109·9	87·9	44·0	12·6	1·6	402·1

$\nu = 6$, $\chi^2 = 38\cdot8$, $P < 0\cdot001$. Hypothesis rejected.

Chapter 9

Question 1 (*page* 147). Because the correlation is negative; hence, as one variate increases, the other tends to decrease.

Exercise 9a (*page* 147)

1. Consider the fathers with height in a given interval (greater than the population mean); their sons will, on the average, be less than the mid-height of the interval but other sons will fall in this interval from fathers who do not fall in the interval. Thus, if the mean height is static, the proportion of men in the interval remains approximately constant.
2. Weight on height; the question is, 'Given my height, what should I weigh?' Approximately linear but slightly convex to the axis of height.

3. $y = \frac{1}{2}x$, $y = 2x$, $\frac{1}{2}$.

4. (i), (iii): angle between regression lines small. (ii): angle between regression lines approaching $90°$.

5. $y - 25{\cdot}7 = 0{\cdot}710\,(x - 28{\cdot}6)$; $\quad y - 25{\cdot}7 = 1{\cdot}15\,(x - 28{\cdot}6)$.

Exercise 9b (*page* 150)

2. See above.

3. $\frac{1}{2}$, $0{\cdot}27(5)$.

6. $y - m_y = r\dfrac{s_y}{s_x}(x - m_x)$.

Exercise 9c (*page* 154)

1. Their sum.

4. $0{\cdot}731$.

Exercise 9d (*page* 155)

1.

r	0	0·5	0·75	0·80	0·90	0·95	0·99
% error remaining	100	86·6	66·1	60·0	43·6	31·2	14·1

2. $\eta_{xy}^2 = 1 - \dfrac{s_x'^2}{s_x^2}$

A measure of correlation should measure the association between values of the variates; in graphical terms, this is the closeness of points on the scatter diagram to the regression curves. This means that r is inappropriate if regression is non-linear.

S_y^2 is based on linear regression (see §9.6).

3. $0{\cdot}86$.

4. (i) $\dfrac{1}{\sigma_x\sqrt{(2\pi)}}\exp\left(-\dfrac{1}{2}\dfrac{x^2}{\sigma_x^2}\right)\delta x,$

(ii) $\dfrac{1}{\sigma_y\sqrt{(1-\rho^2)}\sqrt{(2\pi)}}\exp\left\{-\dfrac{1}{2}\dfrac{\{y-\rho\,(\sigma_y/\sigma_x)\,x\}^2}{\sigma_y^2(1-\rho^2)}\right\}\delta y,$

(iii) $\dfrac{1}{\sigma_x\sigma_y\,2\pi\sqrt{(1-\rho^2)}}\exp\left\{\dfrac{-1}{2(1-\rho^2)}\left(\dfrac{x^2}{\sigma_x^2}-\dfrac{2\rho xy}{\sigma_x\sigma_y}+\dfrac{y^2}{\sigma_y^2}\right)\right\}\delta x\,\delta y.$

Chapter 10

Exercise 10b (*page* 162)

1. (i) $F = 2{\cdot}80$. Not significant. (ii) $F = 5{\cdot}33$. Significant at 5 per cent level.

2. $F = 2{\cdot}12$, $\nu_1 = 30$, $\nu_2 = 29$. Significant at 1 per cent level. (Use **(28)** to estimate variances.)

3. $F = 2{\cdot}79$, $\nu_1 = 21$, $\nu_2 = 23$. P very close to $0{\cdot}01$. (Multiply given variances by $n/(n-1)$ so that **(28)** is used.)

Exercise 10c (*page* 165)

1. $F = 14$, $v_1 = 3$, $v_2 = 223$. Highly significant.

2. 71342   53·8 $F = 1·62$, $v_1 = 5$, $v_2 = 1209$. Not significant.
   58952   912·1

3. Variance between stations less than variance within stations. Not significant—but see also Exercise 10d, No. 4.

4. $F = 2·54$, $v_1 = 7$, $v_2 = 56$. Significant at 5 per cent level. Rate of dispensation not very steady.

5. 1576   1·5755   6985   3073·1 $F = 68·2$, $v_1 = 5$, $v_2 = 16986$.
    909   0·9054   2207   1461·9
Highly significant—hypothesis rejected.

Question 1. (*page* 169). $(h-1)(k-1)$.

Exercise 10d (*page* 173)

1. No. Change of origin does not affect variance; change of unit alters each variance by the same factor.

2. Peas: $F = 0·48$, $v_1 = 4$, $v_2 = 16$. Not significant.
Fertilisers: $F = 3·17$, $v_1 = 4$, $v_2 = 16$. Significant at 5 per cent level.

3. Sides: $F = 3·37$, $v_1 = 2$, $v_2 = 8$. Not significant.
Pupils: $F = 10·31$, $v_1 = 4$, $v_2 = 8$. Significant at 1 per cent level.

4. $F = 29·5$, $v_1 = 11$, $v_2 = 44$. Highly significant. No.

5. Days: $F = 2·09$, $v_1 = 4$, $v_2 = 28$. Not significant.
Hours: $F = 0·34$, $v_1 = 7$, $v_2 = 28$. Not significant.

Table A. Area under the normal curve.

The area given is

$$\int_{-\infty}^{z} \frac{1}{\sqrt{(2\pi)}} e^{-\frac{1}{2}z^2} dz.$$

	0·00	0·01	0·02	0·03	0·04	0·05	0·06	0·07	0·08	0·09
0·0	0·5000	5040	5080	5120	5160	5199	5239	5279	5319	5359
0·1	0·5398	5438	5478	5517	5557	5596	5636	5675	5714	5753
0·2	0·5793	5832	5871	5910	5948	5987	6026	6064	6103	6141
0·3	0·6179	6217	6255	6293	6331	6368	6406	6443	6480	6517
0·4	0·6554	6591	6628	6664	6700	6736	6772	6808	6844	6879
0·5	0·6915	6950	6985	7019	7054	7088	7123	7157	7190	7224
0·6	0·7257	7291	7324	7357	7389	7422	7454	7486	7517	7549
0·7	0·7580	7611	7642	7673	7704	7734	7764	7794	7823	7852
0·8	0·7881	7910	7939	7967	7995	8023	8051	8078	8106	8133
0·9	0·8159	8186	8212	8238	8264	8289	8315	8340	8365	8389
1·0	0·8413	8438	8461	8485	8508	8531	8554	8577	8599	8621
1·1	0·8643	8665	8686	8708	8729	8749	8770	8790	8810	8830
1·2	0·8849	8869	8888	8907	8925	8944	8962	8980	8997	9015
1·3	0·9032	9049	9066	9082	9099	9115	9131	9147	9162	9177
1·4	0·9192	9207	9222	9236	9251	9265	9279	9292	9306	9319
1·5	0·9332	9345	9357	9370	9382	9394	9406	9418	9429	9441
1·6	0·9452	9463	9474	9484	9495	9505	9515	9525	9535	9545
1·7	0·9554	9564	9573	9582	9591	9599	9608	9616	9625	9633
1·8	0·9641	9649	9656	9664	9671	9678	9686	9693	9699	9706
1·9	0·9713	9719	9726	9732	9738	9744	9750	9756	9761	9767
2·0	0·9772	9778	9783	9788	9793	9798	9803	9808	9812	9817
2·1	0·9821	9826	9830	9834	9838	9842	9846	9850	9854	9857
2·2	0·9861	9864	9868	9871	9875	9878	9881	9884	9887	9890
2·3	0·9893	9896	9898	9901	9904	9906	9909	9911	9913	9916
2·4	0·9918	9920	9922	9925	9927	9929	9931	9932	9934	9936
2·5	0·99379	99396	99413	99430	99446	99461	99477	99492	99506	99520
2·6	0·99534	99547	99560	99573	99585	99598	99609	99621	99632	99643
2·7	0·99653	99664	99674	99683	99693	99702	99711	99720	99728	99736
2·8	0·99744	99752	99760	99767	99774	99781	99788	99795	99801	99807
2·9	0·99813	99819	99825	99831	99836	99841	99846	99851	99856	99861
3·0	0·99865	99869	99874	99878	99882	99886	99889	99893	99897	99900
3·1	0·99903	99906	99910	99913	99916	99918	99921	99924	99926	99929
3·2	0·99931	99934	99936	99938	99940	99942	99944	99946	99948	99950
3·3	0·99952	99953	99955	99957	99958	99960	99961	99962	99964	99965
3·4	0·99966	99968	99969	99970	99971	99972	99973	99974	99975	99976
3·5	0·99977	99978	99978	99979	99980	99981	99981	99982	99983	99983
3·6	0·99984	99985	99985	99986	99986	99987	99987	99988	99988	99989
3·7	0·99989	99990	99990	99990	99991	99991	99992	99992	99992	99992
3·8	0·99993	99993	99993	99994	99994	99994	99994	99995	99995	99995
3·9	0·99995	99995	99996	99996	99996	99996	99996	99996	99997	99997

Table B. Percentage points of the *t* distribution.

The probabilities given are that a random variate should *numerically* exceed *t*.

ν	Probability			
	0·05	**0·02**	**0·01**	**0·001**
1	12·706	31·821	63·657	636·619
2	4·303	6·965	9·925	31·598
3	3·182	4·541	5·841	12·941
4	2·776	3·747	4·604	8·610
5	2·571	3·365	4·032	6·859
6	2·447	3·143	3·707	5·959
7	2·365	2·998	3·499	5·405
8	2·306	2·896	3·355	5·041
9	2·262	2·821	3·250	4·781
10	2·228	2·764	3·169	4·587
11	2·201	2·718	3·106	4·437
12	2·179	2·681	3·055	4·318
13	2·160	2·650	3·012	4·221
14	2·145	2·624	2·977	4·140
15	2·131	2·602	2·947	4·073
16	2·120	2·583	2·921	4·015
17	2·110	2·567	2·898	3·965
18	2·101	2·552	2·878	3·922
19	2·093	2·539	2·861	3·883
20	2·086	2·528	2·845	3·850
21	2·080	2·518	2·831	3·819
22	2·074	2·508	2·819	3·792
23	2·069	2·500	2·807	3·767
24	2·064	2·492	2·797	3·745
25	2·060	2·485	2·787	3·725
26	2·056	2·479	2·779	3·707
27	2·052	2·473	2·771	3·690
28	2·048	2·467	2·763	3·674
29	2·045	2·462	2·756	3·659
30	2·042	2·457	2·750	3·646
40	2·021	2·423	2·704	3·551
60	2·000	2·390	2·660	3·460
120	1·980	2·358	2·617	3·373
∞	1·960	2·326	2·576	3·291

Table B is taken from Table III of R. A. Fisher and F. Yates, *Statistical tables for biological, agricultural, and medical research*, published by Oliver and Boyd, Edinburgh, and by permission of the authors and publishers.

Table C. Percentage points of the χ^2 distribution.

The probabilities given are that a random variate should exceed χ^2.

ν	Probability													
	0·99	0·98	0·95	0·90	0·80	0·70	0·50	0·30	0·20	0·10	0·05	0·02	0·01	0·001
1	$0{\cdot}0^3157$	$0{\cdot}0^3628$	0·00393	0·0158	0·0642	0·148	0·455	1·074	1·642	2·706	3·841	5·412	6·635	10·827
2	0·0201	0·0404	0·103	0·211	0·446	0·713	1·386	2·408	3·219	4·605	5·991	7·824	9·210	13·815
3	0·115	0·185	0·352	0·584	1·005	1·424	2·366	3·665	4·642	6·251	7·815	9·837	11·345	16·268
4	0·297	0·429	0·711	1·064	1·649	2·195	3·357	4·878	5·989	7·779	9·488	11·668	13·277	18·465
5	0·554	0·752	1·145	1·610	2·343	3·000	4·351	6·064	7·289	9·236	11·070	13·388	15·086	20·517
6	0·872	1·134	1·635	2·204	3·070	3·828	5·348	7·231	8·558	10·645	12·592	15·033	16·812	22·457
7	1·239	1·564	2·167	2·833	3·822	4·671	6·346	8·383	9·803	12·017	14·067	16·622	18·475	24·322
8	1·646	2·032	2·733	3·490	4·594	5·527	7·344	9·524	11·030	13·362	15·507	18·168	20·090	26·125
9	2·088	2·532	3·325	4·168	5·380	6·393	8·343	10·656	12·242	14·684	16·919	19·679	21·666	27·877
10	2·558	3·059	3·940	4·865	6·179	7·267	9·342	11·781	13·442	15·987	18·307	21·161	23·209	29·588
11	3·053	3·609	4·575	5·578	6·989	8·148	10·341	12·899	14·631	17·275	19·675	22·618	24·725	31·264
12	3·571	4·178	5·226	6·304	7·807	9·034	11·340	14·011	15·812	18·549	21·026	24·054	26·217	32·909
13	4·107	4·765	5·892	7·042	8·634	9·926	12·340	15·119	16·985	19·812	22·362	25·472	27·688	34·528
14	4·660	5·368	6·571	7·790	9·467	10·821	13·339	16·222	18·151	21·064	23·685	26·873	29·141	36·123
15	5·229	5·985	7·261	8·547	10·307	11·721	14·339	17·322	19·311	22·307	24·996	28·259	30·578	37·697
16	5·812	6·614	7·962	9·312	11·152	12·624	15·338	18·418	20·465	23·542	26·296	29·633	32·000	39·252
17	6·408	7·255	8·672	10·085	12·002	13·531	16·338	19·511	21·615	24·769	27·587	30·995	33·409	40·790
18	7·015	7·906	9·390	10·865	12·857	14·440	17·338	20·601	22·760	25·989	28·869	32·346	34·805	42·312
19	7·633	8·567	10·117	11·651	13·716	15·352	18·338	21·689	23·900	27·204	30·144	33·687	36·191	43·820
20	8·260	9·237	10·851	12·443	14·578	16·266	19·337	22·775	25·038	28·412	31·410	35·020	37·566	45·315
21	8·897	9·915	11·591	13·240	15·445	17·182	20·337	23·858	26·171	29·615	32·671	36·343	38·932	46·797
22	9·542	10·600	12·338	14·041	16·314	18·101	21·337	24·939	27·301	30·813	33·924	37·659	40·289	48·268
23	10·196	11·293	13·091	14·848	17·187	19·021	22·337	26·018	28·429	32·007	35·172	38·968	41·638	49·728
24	10·856	11·992	13·848	15·659	18·062	19·943	23·337	27·096	29·553	33·196	36·415	40·270	42·980	51·179
25	11·524	12·697	14·611	16·473	18·940	20·867	24·337	28·172	30·675	34·382	37·652	41·566	44·314	52·620
26	12·198	13·409	15·379	17·292	19·820	21·792	25·336	29·246	31·795	35·563	38·885	42·856	45·642	54·052
27	12·879	14·125	16·151	18·114	20·703	22·719	26·336	30·319	32·912	36·741	40·113	44·140	46·963	55·476
28	13·565	14·847	16·928	18·939	21·588	23·647	27·336	31·391	34·027	37·916	41·337	45·419	48·278	56·893
29	14·256	15·574	17·708	19·768	22·475	24·577	28·336	32·461	35·139	39·087	42·557	46·693	49·588	58·302
30	14·953	16·306	18·493	20·599	23·364	25·508	29·336	33·530	36·250	40·256	43·773	47·962	50·892	59·703

For larger values of ν, the expression $\sqrt{(2\chi^2)} - \sqrt{(2\nu-1)}$ may be used as a normal deviate with unit variance, remembering that the probability for χ^2 corresponds with that of a single tail of the normal curve.

Table C is taken from Table IV of R. A. Fisher and F. Yates, *Statistical tables for biological, agricultural, and medical research,* published by Oliver and Boyd, Edinburgh, and by permission of the authors and publishers.

Table D (i). Five per cent points of the *F* distribution.

ν_1 must always correspond with the greater mean square.

The probability is 0·05 that a random variate should exceed *F*.

$\nu_1=$	1	2	3	4	5	6	8	12	24	∞
$\nu_2=1$	161·4	199·5	215·7	224·6	230·2	234·0	238·9	243·9	249·0	254·3
2	18·51	19·00	19·16	19·25	19·30	19·33	19·37	19·41	19·45	19·50
3	10·13	9·55	9·28	9·12	9·01	8·94	8·84	8·74	8·64	8·53
4	7·71	6·94	6·59	6·39	6·26	6·16	6·04	5·91	5·77	5·63
5	6·61	5·79	5·41	5·19	5·05	4·95	4·82	4·68	4·53	4·36
6	5·99	5·14	4·76	4·53	4·39	4·28	4·15	4·00	3·84	3·67
7	5·59	4·74	4·35	4·12	3·97	3·87	3·73	3·57	3·41	3·23
8	5·32	4·46	4·07	3·84	3·69	3·58	3·44	3·28	3·12	2·93
9	5·12	4·26	3·86	3·63	3·48	3·37	3·23	3·07	2·90	2·71
10	4·96	4·10	3·71	3·48	3·33	3·22	3·07	2·91	2·74	2·54
11	4·84	3·98	3·59	3·36	3·20	3·09	2·95	2·79	2·61	2·40
12	4·75	3·88	3·49	3·26	3·11	3·00	2·85	2·69	2·50	2·30
13	4·67	3·80	3·41	3·18	3·02	2·92	2·77	2·60	2·42	2·21
14	4·60	3·74	3·34	3·11	2·96	2·85	2·70	2·53	2·35	2·13
15	4·54	3·68	3·29	3·06	2·90	2·79	2·64	2·48	2·29	2·07
16	4·49	3·63	3·24	3·01	2·85	2·74	2·59	2·42	2·24	2·01
17	4·45	3·59	3·20	2·96	2·81	2·70	2·55	2·38	2·19	1·96
18	4·41	3·55	3·16	2·93	2·77	2·66	2·51	2·34	2·15	1·92
19	4·38	3·52	3·13	2·90	2·74	2·63	2·48	2·31	2·11	1·88
20	4·35	3·49	3·10	2·87	2·71	2·60	2·45	2·28	2·08	1·84
21	4·32	3·47	3·07	2·84	2·68	2·57	2·42	2·25	2·05	1·81
22	4·30	3·44	3·05	2·82	2·66	2·55	2·40	2·23	2·03	1·78
23	4·28	3·42	3·03	2·80	2·64	2·53	2·38	2·20	2·00	1·76
24	4·26	3·40	3·01	2·78	2·62	2·51	2·36	2·18	1·98	1·73
25	4·24	3·38	2·99	2·76	2·60	2·49	2·34	2·16	1·96	1·71
26	4·22	3·37	2·98	2·74	2·59	2·47	2·32	2·15	1·95	1·69
27	4·21	3·35	2·96	2·73	2·57	2·46	2·30	2·13	1·93	1·67
28	4·20	3·34	2·95	2·71	2·56	2·44	2·29	2·12	1·91	1·65
29	4·18	3·33	2·93	2·70	2·54	2·43	2·28	2·10	1·90	1·64
30	4·17	3·32	2·92	2·69	2·53	2·42	2·27	2·09	1·89	1·62
40	4·08	3·23	2·84	2·61	2·45	2·34	2·18	2·00	1·79	1·51
60	4·00	3·15	2·76	2·52	2·37	2·25	2·10	1·92	1·70	1·39
120	3·92	3·07	2·68	2·45	2·29	2·17	2·02	1·83	1·61	1·25
∞	3·84	2·99	2·60	2·37	2·21	2·09	1·94	1·75	1·52	1·00

Table D (i) is taken from Table V of R. A. Fisher and F. Yates, *Statistical tables for biological, agricultural, and medical research*, published by Oliver and Boyd, Edinburgh, and by permission of the authors and publishers.

Table D (ii). One per cent points of the *F* distribution.

v_1 must always correspond with the greater mean square.
The probability is 0·01 that a random variate should exceed *F*.

$v_1=$	1	2	3	4	5	6	8	12	24	∞
$v_2=1$	4052	4999	5403	5625	5764	5859	5981	6106	6234	6366
2	98·49	99·00	99·17	99·25	99·30	99·33	99·36	99·42	99·46	99·50
3	34·12	30·81	29·46	28·71	28·24	27·91	27·49	27·05	26·60	26·12
4	21·20	18·00	16·69	15·98	15·52	15·21	14·80	14·37	13·93	13·46
5	16·26	13·27	12·06	11·39	10·97	10·67	10·29	9·89	9·47	9·02
6	13·74	10·92	9·78	9·15	8·75	8·47	8·10	7·72	7·31	6·88
7	12·25	9·55	8·45	7·85	7·46	7·19	6·84	6·47	6·07	5·65
8	11·26	8·65	7·59	7·01	6·63	6·37	6·03	5·67	5·28	4·86
9	10·56	8·02	6·99	6·42	6·06	5·80	5·47	5·11	4·73	4·31
10	10·04	7·56	6·55	5·99	5·64	5·39	5·06	4·71	4·33	3·91
11	9·65	7·20	6·22	5·67	5·32	5·07	4·74	4·40	4·02	3·60
12	9·33	6·93	5·95	5·41	5·06	4·82	4·50	4·16	3·78	3·36
13	9·07	6·70	5·74	5·20	4·86	4·62	4·30	3·96	3·59	3·16
14	8·86	6·51	5·56	5·03	4·69	4·46	4·14	3·80	3·43	3·00
15	8·68	6·36	5·42	4·89	4·56	4·32	4·00	3·67	3·29	2·87
16	8·53	6·23	5·29	4·77	4·44	4·20	3·89	3·55	3·18	2·75
17	8·40	6·11	5·18	4·67	4·34	4·10	3·79	3·45	3·08	2·65
18	8·28	6·01	5·09	4·58	4·25	4·01	3·71	3·37	3·00	2·57
19	8·18	5·93	5·01	4·50	4·17	3·94	3·63	3·30	2·92	2·49
20	8·10	5·85	4·94	4·43	4·10	3·87	3·56	3·23	2·86	2·42
21	8·02	5·78	4·87	4·37	4·04	3·81	3·51	3·17	2·80	2·36
22	7·94	5·72	4·82	4·31	3·99	3·76	3·45	3·12	2·75	2·31
23	7·88	5·66	4·76	4·26	3·94	3·71	3·41	3·07	2·70	2·26
24	7·82	5·61	4·72	4·22	3·90	3·67	3·36	3·03	2·66	2·21
25	7·77	5·57	4·68	4·18	3·86	3·63	3·32	2·99	2·62	2·17
26	7·72	5·53	4·64	4·14	3·82	3·59	3·29	2·96	2·58	2·13
27	7·68	5·49	4·60	4·11	3·78	3·56	3·26	2·93	2·55	2·10
28	7·64	5·45	4·57	4·07	3·75	3·53	3·23	2·90	2·52	2·06
29	7·60	5·42	4·54	4·04	3·73	3·50	3·20	2·87	2·49	2·03
30	7·56	5·39	4·51	4·02	3·70	3·47	3·17	2·84	2·47	2·01
40	7·31	5·18	4·31	3·83	3·51	3·29	2·99	2·66	2·29	1·80
60	7·08	4·98	4·13	3·65	3·34	3·12	2·82	2·50	2·12	1·60
120	6·85	4·79	3·95	3·48	3·17	2·96	2·66	2·34	1·95	1·38
∞	6·64	4·60	3·78	3·32	3·02	2·80	2·51	2·18	1·79	1·00

Table D (ii) is taken from Table V of R. A. Fisher and F. Yates, *Statistical tables for biological, agricultural, and medical research*, published by Oliver and Boyd, Edinburgh, and by permission of the authors and publishers.

Index

Index

List of formulae used for cross reference

Chapter 6

$$r = \frac{\frac{1}{n}\sum f(x-m_x)(y-m_y)}{s_x s_y} \qquad \text{(20a)}^* \quad \text{p. } 96$$

For **(20)**, see p. 91.   For **(21)**, see p. 95.   For **(22a)**, see p. 97.

$$r = \frac{\frac{1}{n}\sum f(x-x_0)(y-y_0) - (m_x - x_0)(m_y - y_0)}{s_x\, s_y} \qquad \text{(22)}^* \quad \text{p. } 97$$

$$\rho = \frac{\sum P(x-\mu_x)(y-\mu_y)}{\sigma_x \sigma_y} \qquad \text{(23)} \quad \text{p. } 102$$

Chapter 7

$$s_{x-y}^2 = s_x^2 + s_y^2 - 2r s_x s_y \qquad \text{(24)}^* \quad \text{p. } 106$$

$$\sigma_{m_x - m_y}^2 = \sigma_{m_x}^2 + \sigma_{m_y}^2 - 2\rho\sigma_{m_x}\sigma_{m_y} \qquad \text{(25)} \quad \text{p. } 107$$

For independent random samples

$$\sigma_{m_x - m_y}^2 \simeq \frac{s_x^2}{n_x} + \frac{s_y^2}{n_y} \qquad \text{(26)} \quad \text{p. } 109$$

For independent random samples

$$\sigma_{p_1 - p_2}^2 = \frac{pq}{n_1} + \frac{pq}{n_2} \qquad \text{(27)} \quad \text{p. } 116$$

$$\hat{\sigma}^2 = \frac{1}{n-1}\sum f(x-m)^2 \qquad \text{(28)} \quad \text{p. } 121$$

Chapter 8 $$\chi_s^2 = \frac{(f_1 - F_1)^2}{F_1} + \frac{(f_2 - F_2)^2}{F_2} + \ldots + \frac{(f_k - F_k)^2}{F_k} \qquad \text{(29)} \quad \text{p. } 131$$

$$y = K e^{-\frac{1}{2}X^2}(\chi^2)^{\frac{1}{2}(\nu-2)} \qquad \text{(30)} \quad \text{p. } 132$$

Number of degrees of freedom

= (number of cells) − (number of linear constraints on the F's)

$$\text{(31)} \quad \text{p. } 139$$

Chapter 9 $$y - m_y = r\frac{s_y}{s_x}(x - m_x) \qquad \text{(32)} \quad \text{p. } 149$$

Chapter 10 $$\frac{\sum_s n_i(m_i - m)^2}{k-1} \qquad \text{(33)} \quad \text{p. } 158$$

$$\frac{\sum f(x-m_i)^2}{n-k} \qquad \text{(34)} \quad \text{p. } 159$$

$$\sum f(x-m)^2 = \sum f(x-m_i)^2 + \sum_s n_i(m_i - m)^2 \qquad \text{(35)} \quad \text{p. } 160$$

$$\sum (x-m)^2 - \sum_c h(_c m_j - m)^2 - \sum_r k(_r m_i - m)^2 \qquad \text{(36)} \quad \text{p. } 168$$

$$\sum (x - _c m_j - _r m_i + m)^2 \qquad \text{(36a)} \quad \text{p. } 169$$

* Similar formulae for theoretical frequency distributions and/or probability distributions may be obtained by replacing m by μ, s by σ, and r by ρ, also f and n as appropriate.